Contents

Index

M·B·C·O·L

MBCOL

www.mbcol.org.uk

2011

The Queen's Golden
Jubilee Award
for
Voluntary Service

Published by MBCOL Ltd.

Foreword

All humans have major life events.

It may be a paradox to describe death as a life event but, unlike other milestones such as marriage or parenthood, death is inevitable.

We prepare for all such milestones and yet perhaps tend to shy away from any proper understanding of death, as it is generally very unwelcome and distressing to consider.

Whilst the immediate prelude to death may be shared, death itself is a uniquely individual experience.

In contrast the processes, rituals and social and legal procedures following death are burdens that fall upon relatives and friends who have to organize the consequences of death, often in the throes of the emotions and sorrows of bereavement.

Having been involved for many years in international criminal law, where cases involving sometimes very large scale deaths and killings are part of the evidential fabric, and witnesses to awful events are often traumatized and confused, the need for understanding and accommodating this complex part of the human condition has become all the more obvious to me.

This excellent and informative book provides practical answers to many of the questions and anxieties that arise as well as being a fascinating account of the subject from so many varying perspectives.

It will help the reader both understand and cope with the concepts and the consequences and should be on the bookshelf of every medical professional, police officer, social worker, lawyer, religious leader, teaching staff and indeed, anyone who has any doubts as to their understanding of this complicated and essential subject.

I have been fortunate to come to know Suleman Nagdi through his work within the communities of Leicester over a number of years. He is one of those very rare and special, determined and hardworking men who go sensitively through life impressing, enlightening and assisting all those with whom he comes into contact with.

Judge Howard Morrison CBE QC

International Court
The Hague - Netherlands

Endorsements

In my capacity as the Diversity & Community Relations Judge, I have come to know the invaluable work that has been done by the Muslim Burial Council of Leicestershire (MBCOL), good luck with this publication. Its Chairman, Suleman Nagdi MBE DL, has led and fostered the need to understand each other. This has struck a particular chord in my own work that deals with the many aspects of diversity. I know that MBCOL strives to reach pragmatic and sensitive arrangements for burial.

This book highlights the critical importance of promoting good community relations both locally, nationally and internationally. It is a well-researched book, which has drawn together the needs of many faiths and belief systems to ensure that their burial wishes are respected and accommodated. It covers the formalities required in law, burial and cremation procedures, bereavement and mourning and the sensitive issue of autopsies. It is interesting to note how much common ground there is among people.

With knowledge comes understanding and with understanding and respect can come an accommodation. I feel that it would serve as an excellent reference publication for individuals and public servants.

It gives me great pleasure to commend this splendid book.

His Honour Judge Simon Hammond
Diversity & Community Relations Judge

It gives me great pleasure to support the publication of this guide, which seeks to help inform a wide range of healthcare service professionals including hospices, hospitals, care and nursing homes in all aspects of dealing with end of life care, the burial and cremation process for different religious groups as well as providing valuable information to members of the wider community.

While we accept that death is inevitable for all of us, few of us give thought to what needs to happen when that time comes and few have given consideration to the issue of burial or cremation. This guide provides valuable information on the needs that should be considered for different faith groups and I believe will help health service professionals and providers to understand those needs as well as benefit people in our diverse communities. This publication is informative and provides a much broader understanding of the sensitivities involved around caring for different religious groups and will be a valuable resource to healthcare professionals and help them to provide a more person centred approach to care at bereavement. This guide deals sensitively with all aspects of death.

By better understanding the religious and culture differences of a patient healthcare professionals and providers will be able to offer the right kind of support and care to those patients and to their families at the point of bereavement and beyond.

This guide makes a valuable contribution to the twin goals of building cohesive communities and promoting high quality care for all at the end of their life.

Surinder Mohan Sharma

National Director for Equality and Human Rights
Department of Health

Preface

As the United Kingdom becomes increasingly multicultural and embraces the vibrancy that difference brings with it, recognition and understanding of different cultural and religious needs become ever more important.

We have made considerable progress in many aspects of public life such as business and sport. However within the private realm, challenges remain. These are perhaps never more acute than at the time of death, when people feel most vulnerable and much help and support is required. Healthcare professionals (usually in hospitals and hospices), will frequently encounter patients with terminal conditions, who require healthcare which is sensitive to their religious and spiritual needs. By knowing the religion and culture of a patient, the service provider can ensure that the care given remains very much patient centred. This insight can also go some way in aiding communication and understanding of the patient's needs.

This publication will assist a wide range of health service providers including hospices, hospitals, care and nursing homes, hostels, supported accommodation services, community health centres, district nursing, doctors, police, local and central government.

I hope that this book will be helpful to academic institutions with an interest in the subject and a useful resource for those engaged in the area of health and behavioural sciences and it would be an excellent reference guide on education courses and a variety of training programmes. More importantly, I believe that this book will be of practical benefit to the wider community. Its circulation is intended to include places of worship, libraries, community and voluntary groups, resource and education centres, as well as individuals and families facing death and bereavement.

Death is inevitable for all. Few people however think about death in their everyday lives, perhaps partly because we are fortunate enough not to see it as frequently as our predecessors did or as many still do in different parts of the world. Perhaps this is also because it is easier to focus on our present situation, rather than on what we may feel we do not know enough about. Then of course there is the fear of death and what will happen afterwards, as well as what happens to the loved ones left behind. This can mean that when we are faced with death, an understanding of what to do, and how to do it, what to feel and how to express it, is limited. Added to this, the prospect of trying to decipher what rites and responsibilities one's faith or belief may require can be both complicated and daunting.

"DISCOVERING THROUGH DEATH – Beliefs and Practices" has been written from different belief perspectives and aims to address some of these issues. It gives a better understanding of what people of faith and those of no faith believe happens after death. It also deals with what should or should not be done to the body of the deceased, how disposal procedures should take place, how grief may be dealt with and much more. It also looks at some of the debates around complex issues such as post mortems, organ transplants, brain death and suicide.

There is currently insufficient information available in a form that identifies the practices of different belief systems in a consistent manner. In this respect, this book is pioneering in its approach. There are important differences in the needs of different cultural and religious groups for palliative care, terminal care, handling of the body immediately after death, funeral arrangements and spiritual needs.

There are variations within the text writing about different religions in an appropriate way. An example of this is differences, such as the description of the Almighty as "G-d" within Judaism.

I have managed to draw and source the material from many quarters, including academics, lay people, faith leaders, professionals, civil servants and those that I consider to be dedicated friends. I have received contributions from various religious institutions and representatives locally and nationally. I am grateful for their help and support.

I recognise that there may be some variations on emphasis and practice around death amongst people of the same faith tradition. There may be internal diversity and therefore variations in rites and customs due for example to an individual's own cultural or personal interpretation. Whilst I cannot be exhaustive in all of these interpretations this study offers an insight into the main practices and implications of death and bereavement.

The religious requirements are written within the context of the legal system of this country, which is vitally important. It is my hope that this book will be useful for any organisation that employs and/ or provides services for people from diverse faith communities. I believe the value of a resource of this kind cannot be underestimated, for one's belief is a powerful force in influencing and shaping the attitude and response to death and bereavement and how one copes with it and therefore it is vital for those working in the community to have an awareness of the varying faith perspectives for many people in this country.

In many belief systems death is a continuation of life and a gateway to a different form of existence. It also marks the end of what is hoped to have been a rich and fulfilling life. For many people, understanding of what happens to a person after death not only provides hope, but also instils a sense of peace that enables them to continue with their own life. Rituals around the death process can also be very soothing. Some may be very public and demonstrative affairs, whilst others are much more private. Mourning for some may be conducted in a very structured form over a set period of time to enable closure, for others there is no structure or time limit and is left to the pace of each individual or family.

I recognise that some religions are influenced by the cultural environment from which they have originated. It is important to bear this context in mind when trying to understand certain cultural requirements. One way that this may exhibit itself is when a patient is close to death.

In some cultures (or religions) being with their loved one at this crucial time becomes paramount as it is believed that their presence will ease the death. This can mean quite large numbers of people coming to visit the patient, some of whom will insist they want to stay with them. Depriving someone of the final opportunity to provide comfort and support to their loved ones in their final moments could result in a great deal of distress. Rituals (or acts) may be formalised and carried out by the spiritual leader or practitioner. These include the carrying out of specific acts and the use of symbolic artefacts (e.g. holy water and rosary beads). These requirements are vital to the needs of people and must be accommodated. Such sensitivities should be borne in mind because this underpins and supports the physical, emotional and spiritual wellbeing. Hence health professionals are reminded that a holistic approach to care is required.

Many hospitals in the UK now employ faith chaplains or authorised hospital visitors who can aid in providing appropriate spiritual support for individuals and families, or at least know where to obtain it. Multi faith prayer rooms are also becoming increasingly available but patients and families may not be aware of such resources.

A prerequisite to using this book is the understanding that a number of religions cross language and cultural boundaries. Not all Christians are white and speak English; likewise not all Muslims are brown and speak Urdu, Gujarati or Bengali. To complicate things further, it cannot be assumed that a person of faith, be they Hindu, Sikh or Baha'i etc would automatically desire to follow set procedures and requirements of that faith perspective, they might be more relaxed about such rulings.

Likewise it is important not to make generalisations about those who consciously practise their faith. There can be differences of opinion even within the same religion, not all people of the same faith practise the same rituals or follow the same school of thought. As with many other aspects to our lives that make us individual, there are choices and paths followed within each faith group. I feel that it is important that the family and friends of the deceased, as well as service providers, try to acquire some basic knowledge about each individual's situation to ensure a sensitive approach is taken when working with people nearing the end of their lives.

A person's ability to make decisions and implement them through their own conscious and cognitive competence is of utmost importance for all beliefs. This is my understanding of proper consent. However, when such consent cannot be secured, close family members will be required to take responsibility for decisions. In the absence of family this may be delegated to religious and lay leaders in the community, who may assume the guardianship of the person's rights in so far as they relate to matters of faith. This may be subject to intervention by the Court, who will take all matters into account.

I would also like to highlight the many possible barriers in patient care. There may be issues surrounding access and service provision to those from minority groups. The reasons are often complex and may include matters such as language, inadequate advocacy, financial constraints, inadequate staff training and transport difficulties. These barriers could be met by a variety of means. This may include a greater recruitment of healthcare personnel from ethnic minority groups, comprehensive staff training on religion, and belief and greater involvement of individuals from minority communities in planning and delivering care.

The enormity of undertaking the task from both religious and cultural aspects of death and dying was beyond the scope of one single person. Therefore, I take this opportunity to thank all those who have contributed and I have mentioned them at the end. The work that I have had to undertake and the completion of this book could not have occurred without the good working relationships that I have mange to foster between many people of different cultures and beliefs.

I also like to mention my friend Faizal Essat, who I believe deserves recognition at this point. I can recall the many hours that we spent together working on this project, I acknowledge the precious family time that he gave up to assist. He is my critical friend who is always honest in his advice and sincere in his support. (He also made endless cups of tea often late into the early hours of the morning.) I know that Faizal will be embarrassed by my words; I am keen to recognise him now as I value his contribution.

The intention is for the arrangement of the material in this handbook to be concise, straightforward and logical. In order to maintain continuity and improve readability, its contents are divided into sections for each of the beliefs.

In my experience, drawn from many years of working in the community with people of all backgrounds, races and religions, I have come to recognise that respect of diversity comes not by seeing everyone as the same but through exploring and understanding differences. Only then can we truly respect and appreciate one another and gain the hope of understanding each other better. I do not believes that engaging with other faiths leads to a dilution of my own belief. For me personally, my encounter with others has fortified my own faith and relationship with Allah. I pray that we all grow in the spirit of humanity and good works with our fellow man.

Suleman Nagdi MBE JP DL
Chairman - Muslim Burial Council of Leicestershire

Muslim Burial Council of Leicestershire (MBCOL) Background

The rationale behind this unique book goes back to 2005 when the Muslim Burial Council of Leicestershire (MBCOL) published 'Guidelines on Death and Burial of a Muslim'. This book was promoted and distributed throughout the community and to statutory bodies. Two years later, MBCOL's desire was to produce a more in depth publication as a follow up. Our commitment to work with the wider community is well known. Therefore a book to encompass all beliefs was a natural progression.

Our Board of Trustees and Advisors had no hesitation in taking this idea forward. We then began our journey of approaching supporters to enable the creation of the book. In order to understand the book, the reader needs to understand the reasons behind MBCOL's creation, historical and current UK legislation in relation to burials and an analysis of the modern day challenges.

MBCOL was set up in Leicester in August 1994. In October 1995, MBCOL signed a historic legal agreement with Leicester City Council to deliver a comprehensive burial service and other related work.

Our work has developed over the years and to appreciate the subject fully it is useful to focus on the legislative changes and the history of death and bereavement services.

An obvious starting point in relation to legislation is the Human Rights Act of 1998. This Act of Parliament gave legal effect to citizens of the UK to fundamental rights and freedoms. These fundamental rights or freedoms were initially set out in the European Convention on Human Rights. These rights not only affect matters of life and death, like freedom from torture and killing, but also those rights in everyday life in terms of what to do or not to do. The human rights that are dealt with under this piece of legislation are as follows:

- The right to life

- Freedom from torture and degrading treatment

- Freedom from slavery and forced labour

- The right to liberty

- The right to a fair trial

- The right not to be punished for something that was not a crime when you did it

- The right to respect for private family life

- The freedom of thought, conscience and religion

- Freedom of expression

- Freedom of assembly and association

- The right to marry or form a civil partnership and start a family

- The right not to be discriminated against in respect of these freedoms

- The right to own property

- The right to an education

- The right to participate in free elections

One can see that the rights listed above are fairly wide ranging and cover various spheres of our lives. The one that we are concerned with in relation to the work of MBCOL is the freedom related to religion. Many have attempted to encapsulate a definitive explanation as to what this means. One possible definition is that freedom of religion is the freedom of an individual or community, in public or private, to manifest religion or belief in teaching, practice, worship and observance. It is generally recognised also to include freedom to change religion or to follow no religion. Freedom of religion is therefore considered by many in our world today as a fundamental human right.

This sentiment can be seen in the Equality and Human Rights Commission report "Bringing people together" which states;

"Helping people to achieve social change and ensuring organisations can meet their legal and moral responsibilities under equality legislation and the Human Rights Act"

This then brings us to our diverse communities in the UK. These are drawn from numerous cultural, social, faith and non faith backgrounds. These communities have various needs depending on their own particular background, culture and beliefs.

Another key piece of legislation is the Burial Act of 1857. This Act was passed in Parliament and its purpose was to regulate burial grounds. This act also regulated how the deceased were to be buried and provided specific rules in relation to the exhumation of remains. Prior to this landmark piece of legislation the practice of burial was remarkably different.

From about the 7th Century in most European countries, including Britain, burial was under the control of the Church and could only take place on consecrated church ground. These practices varied slightly, but on the whole, bodies were usually buried in mass graves until they de-composed. The bones would then be exhumed, collected and stored in ossuaries, either along the arcaded boundary walls of the churchyard, or within the church under floor slabs and behind walls. An ossuary is a chest or a building or sometimes a disused well.

At about this time the business of burial was often inextricably linked with one's social status. Members of the nobility, and other individuals of high status, would be buried in individual crypts inside or beneath the relevant place of worship, which would usually be the Church. The crypt would be marked with the individual's name and date of death. In Europe this was often accompanied with a depiction of the family coat of arms and other such insignia.

Changes then occurred in the late 18th and early 19th Century. These led to the creation of burial grounds as we see them today.

Accordingly, the responsibility to provide funerals and to bury the deceased fell on local authorities. In fact, in most of Europe new places of burial were established away from heavily populated areas and outside town or city boundaries. Nowadays many such cemeteries have become municipally owned and are thus independent of Churches [and Church yards.]

Today, dealing with interment of bodies and burials in the UK is very much a multi agency task. We have local authorities that regulate burial ground. When a death occurs the Police may be involved and even the Coroner's office can become engaged, if appropriate. The Coroner seeks to establish the cause of death. The Registrar of Births, Deaths and Marriages has specific obligations to ensure that there is proper recording of deaths. All these agencies need to engage and work together.

MBCOL, as an organisation, fits into this multi agency arrangement in that under its legal agreement with the local authority it has delegated responsibility to carry out administrative functions, such as producing documentation to facilitate early burials. These statutory agencies have recognised the needs of the various communities and have identified and co-operated in the implementation of an 'out of hours' burial service. Without the co-operation of these agencies it would not be possible to make arrangements for early burial. The engagement of the community in these types of service is underlined in the words of Rt. Hon Hazel Blears MP. (Communities in control - Real People Real Power – Communities and Local Government July 2008).

"We want to see public services and public servants in tune with, and accountable to, the people they serve"

There is unfortunately a misconception that the idea of swift burials is only required by the laws of the Muslim faith. This is untrue. Other faiths such as Judaism also have this requirement, and cultural groups such as Christians of South Asian origin also endorse the concept of early burial. This is something that should be offered as a choice to those who feel that they require it.

The work of MBCOL, to fulfil the above successfully, has led to the organisation contributing at national and international level. This was recognised in June 2007, when MBCOL received recognition from Her Majesty the Queen in being awarded the Queen's Award for Voluntary Service. This honour recognised the pivotal and important work that MBCOL has undertaken in going beyond simply providing an out of hours burial service. Our achievements fit the views expressed generally, and in particular, by the Prime Minister Rt. Hon. Gordon Brown MP. *(Communities in control - Real People Real Power – Communities and Local Government July 2008).*

"It is an agenda for empowerment that reaches right across the board, from supporting people who want to take an active role in their communities"....... "the chance to get more involved in key public service"

Support for MBCOL with the issue of near virtual autopsy is gathering pace. This involves replacing traditional invasive post mortems with modern scanning techniques. We are working with the University of Leicester and the Department of Health on this. We hope that this approach will be implemented nationally. Traditional autopsies, due to their invasive nature, can be very distressing to families. These feelings were clearly felt during the organ retention scandal at Alder Hey Hospital. Our work with the University has been fully supported by many major faith institutions particularly the Jewish community. We are confident that if proven successful, virtual autopsies could change the face of pathology around the world.

Our first bereavement book (Guidelines on Death & Burial of a Muslim) was based on our encounters with situations where bereaved families were not familiar with the law, proper rites of the preparation and burial of a loved one and the obligations of statutory organisations. As the UK becomes increasingly diverse, these difficulties will be faced by other faith communities as well. The book also delivers on two of the recommendations made in "Embracing the present, planning the future, social action by the faith communities of Leicester" (Ravat, R 2004). First of all we meet the recommendation of promoting 'mentoring within the faith communities' because our good practice is already being disseminated to all faith communities, not least through this book and its subsequent promotion. The book also responds to the suggestion for 'faith awareness programmes to be included in equal opportunities training' because the book is a vital training tool for public service providers such as nursing staff in hospitals, care homes and hospices.

MBCOL provides hands-on information, help and assistance to every member of the community relating to interment, and liaises with organisations to enable the community to access suitable interment services and practices.

MBCOL has contributed to a number of high profile consultations at local, national and international levels. Examples include work with the Home Office on the future of burial grounds, a House of Lords inquiry into organ donation and transplantation and a Ministry of Justice review of the statutory duties when reporting deaths. It furthers the study of the use of MRI and CT scanning as an alternative to invasive autopsies.

For further more detailed information on MBCOL's work can be found at www.mbcol.org.uk

I wish to thank my fellow Board members of MBCOL for their support and strategic vision for this project. They are Dr. Rashed Akhtar, Yakoob Dassu, Hashim Duale, Zubair Hassam, Mohamed Omarji, Rafique Patel, Adam Sabat and Sikandar Sattar.

Suleman Nagdi MBE JP DL

Spotlight on Local Good Practice

H.M. Coroner Leicester City and South Leicestershire

We have recognised the importance of the role that can be played by the Coroner. Mrs Catherine Mason was appointed Her Majesty's Coroner for Leicester City and South Leicestershire in March 2009. With her appointment the Office of the Coroner moved from a part to a full time position.

Mrs Mason comes from a nursing background who went on to study Law. She qualified as a solicitor practising Personal Injury and Medical Negligence.

In the short time that I have known her, I have found her to be passionate about the Coronial service and is dedicated to improving the service within her jurisdiction. She hopes that the people of Leicester will get to know her as a caring Coroner who is sensitive to their cultural and faith needs. She also hopes that should they come into contact with her at any time during bereavement, they will have the confidence and trust in being cared for and supported through this very traumatic time.

Since being appointed, Mrs Mason has reduced the number of post-mortem examinations by no less than a third. This is a remarkable achievement brought about by taking a direct one to one approach with the Doctors and talking to them when they refer a death. This is a significant achievement, and we welcome these results.

Mrs Mason recognises the importance in some communities to have the deceased returned to loved ones as soon as possible. She also recognises that early burial within these communities is essential and a religious requirement. More importantly she is aware that it avoids further distress to family members. In this effort she has boldly formulated and introduced an out of hours system of accessing the services of the Coroner. In practical terms this means that deaths can be referred to the Coroner out of hours if there is a need for release of the deceased and registration of the death to enable weekend and bank holiday funerals. This system is available 24 hours, 7 days a week (except Good Friday, Easter Monday and Christmas Day).

Other important changes introduced by Mrs Mason are in relation to deaths at home and post-mortem procedures. In relation to deaths at home police officers are no longer required to attend every sudden death in the community. All sudden and unexpected deaths will be attended to by the East Midlands Ambulance Service (EMAS), unless there is a medical general practitioner (GP) on scene who is already dealing with the situation. The EMAS staff will, as they do now, confirm death (but not confirm cause of death) and forward the necessary documentation to the Coroner's officers. Leicestershire Constabulary officers will not attend the death unless the EMAS staff consider the circumstances to be suspicious or cannot be explained. In such circumstances EMAS staff will alert the police and the circumstances will be investigated fully. The sudden death of a loved one is a stressful experience for relatives and family members. Police attendance can sometimes be seen as intrusive, often delaying the process of the Coroner's removal of the deceased to a suitable place of rest. This new process of dealing with deaths at home will have many benefits. Families of the deceased should experience a faster process of the death being attended to and dealt with. There will usually be no police involvement and the opportunity for the perceived stigma of police officers being at the scene of a death will in time be diminished.

In relation to post-mortems it has been agreed with the University Hospitals Leicester (UHL) Pathologists that before a post-mortem is conducted there is to be a review of the deceased medical records. If in their professional opinion a cause of death is known, the pathologists will do a "view and cause" and not perform a formal invasive post-mortem.

Furthermore Mrs Mason's office is looking favourably at the application of MRI or CT as an alternative to invasive autopsies, now commonly known as "virtual autopsy". She is working closely with a senior pathologist, Professor Guy Rutty, from the University of Leicester and who is a recognised authority on MRI. She is aware of the limitations of this process when addressing deaths that are related to trauma and those to natural causes.

Mrs Mason intends to apply further changes to Leicester's Coronial system. Some of these changes relate to staff restructuring once all staff are employed by the Local Authority. This will give a more efficient service and one that can cope better with short notice absence through sickness. A web site is also soon to be commissioned in order to provide detailed information on the services provided by the Coroner's office. The website will also provide details on out of hours contact numbers etc.

The changes brought about since Mrs Mason's appointment have indeed been remarkable, especially when one considers the short time within which these changes have taken place. She is a confident individual who is driven by dedication and a philosophy, which is to always treat others, as she would wish her and her family to be treated.

In the course of my discussions with her I know that Mrs Mason welcomes the close relationship that has developed between her and MBCOL and also supports the joint initiatives that have taken place as a result. She very much hopes that it will continue and strengthen as time goes on. She believes that it is in all our interests that we continue to work together to take the Coronial service in Leicester forward and ensure that it is fit for purpose and second to none.

It is my hope that this approach can be adopted throughout the country and serve as good practice and demonstrate how communities can work together for the common good.

Suleman Nagdi MBE JP DL

East Midlands Ambulance Service NHS Trust (EMAS)

The ambulance trust provides emergency care in response to over half a million 999 calls each year. Sometimes these 999 calls involve the death of a person.

In Leicester, Leicestershire and Rutland all sudden and unexpected deaths will be attended by EMAS unless there is a GP (medical general practitioner) on scene who is already dealing with the situation.

Where death occurs, EMAS staff will always act respectfully towards the deceased person and towards their family, relatives and friends who are present.

EMAS staff also act in accordance with the requirements of the Coroner. The information below relates to deaths in the community in which EMAS is involved in Leicester, Leicestershire and Rutland.

1. If the diagnosis of death is made by EMAS staff at the deceased person's home:

- Following the diagnosis of death by the EMAS Technician or Paramedic attending, the EMAS member of staff will complete a 'Fact of Death' form.

- The attending crew, or the EMAS Ambulance Control Centre (which takes all 999 telephone calls) will contact the deceased person's GP, or if applicable the Out of Hours medical service provider, to inform them of the death.

  This action will be recorded by the ambulance service crew on the Fact of Death form.

- If the GP is not going to attend, the ambulance crew will advise the relative or carer to contact their preferred funeral director to arrange the removal of the deceased person.

If the relative or carer requires help with this process, the ambulance service crew may provide this help, either themselves or via Ambulance Control.

- If the EMAS crew believes that the family or carers of the deceased person are well supported, they will not normally wait at the scene for the GP to attend.

- Before they leave the scene, the EMAS crew will ensure that appropriate arrangements for the removal of the deceased person have been made.

- There are some circumstances where the Police *will* attend a sudden and unexpected death. These circumstances include, amongst others, the following: where the circumstances are suspicious or cannot be explained; where the deceased is under 18 years of age; where a relative or other responsible person is not easily contactable.

  The further circumstances where the Police will be called to attend include fatal road traffic collisions, and this is detailed in the next section.

2. If the diagnosis of death is made at a road traffic collision:

- If the road is closed and the scene is secured by the Police, and provided there is no public access that allows views of the deceased person or persons, EMAS ambulance crews will only remove the body of the deceased person in exceptional circumstances after consultation with the Police's Senior Investigating Officer.

  This is at the request of the Police and is related to accident investigation and continuity of evidence.

- In normal circumstances following the pronouncement of the fact of death, the Police will assume responsibility for the body of the deceased person and arrange removal by their Duty Undertakers.

The Police will be responsible for notifying the relevant Coroner, but the EMAS crew will complete a Fact of Death form.

3. If the person dies whilst in transit or upon arrival at a hospital Accident & Emergency department:

- All attempts will be made to resuscitate the patient, unless otherwise specified in a formal 'End of Life Agreement' (*see 'End of Life Care Registration System' below*).

- The ambulance personnel attending the patient will diagnose the fact of death in accordance with EMAS procedure (if at hospital this will be done in conjunction with the hospital's staff).

- Once the EMAS Paramedic or Technician has diagnosed the fact of death and completed all the relevant documentation, they will inform the Coroner.

End of Life Care Registration System

Since 2008, EMAS has been working with GPs to develop a system to allow the easy communication of End of Life Decisions with the ambulance service.

This helps to avoid situations where treatments such as cardiopulmonary resuscitation might otherwise be commenced when they are either inappropriate or are against the wishes of the patient.

The EMAS system can also cover Advanced Decisions to Refuse Treatment.

Operating *only* with the full involvement of GPs, the procedures involve detailed instructions being contained within a care plan which is left in the person's / patient's home or place of residence.

You can find out more about End of Life Care Decisions and all other aspects of the work of the East Midlands Ambulance Service by visiting us at our website:
www.emas.nhs.uk

The information in this section was kindly provided by Robert Walker, EMAS

Death Certification & Registration

All deaths in this country have to follow set statutory procedures. The following sets out the basic information which we hope will be helpful.

A death certificate is necessary as this is a primary enabling document without which further steps cannot be taken. This can be obtained with the necessary input from the medical profession. The doctor who treated the person during their last illness will usually issue a medical certificate of cause of death.

There is a legal duty on medical practitioners to issue a certificate of cause of death. This is governed by Section 22 of the Births and Deaths Registration Act 1953. This provides that

In the case of the death of any person who has been attended during his last illness by a registered medical practitioner, that practitioner shall sign a certificate in the prescribed form stating to the best of his knowledge and belief the cause of death and shall forthwith deliver that certificate to the registrar.

This will not occur if the death is one that becomes the subject of a report to the Coroner or if an inquest then subsequently occurs

You should give the cause of death certificate to the Registrar of Births and Deaths for the district where the person died. All deaths have to be registered and must be registered by the local Registrar. There are some variations depending on the particular circumstances as follows:

If the death has been reported to the Coroner

You will need to wait until the Registrar has a certificate from the Coroner. You will be told if this is the case.

Who can register the death?

The following people can register a person's death:

- A relative

- Someone who was with the person when they died

- Someone who is arranging the funeral (but not a Funeral Director)

It is possible for other people to register the death in certain circumstances. If you are unsure whether you can register, please telephone the Register Office and they will be able to advise you.

Where should you register?

You should register a death with the Registrar of Births and Deaths for the district where the person died.

Do I need to make an appointment?

Yes, you should contact your local Registrars office to make an appointment.

When should I register a death?

You should usually register a death within 5 days. However, in exceptional circumstances, the Registrar may agree to delay this.

What information will the registrar ask for?

The Registrar will need the following information about the person who has died:

- The date of their death

- Where they died

- Their full name – and any previous names they used

- Their date of birth and where they were born (usually just the town and county)

- Their occupation – if now retired, the last or main occupation before retirement

- Their address

- Your name and address

If the person who died was a married woman, the Registrar will also need to know:

- Her maiden surname

- Her husband's full name

- Her husband's occupation – if retired, the last or main occupation before retirement.

Other general information

The Registrar will also ask if the person who has died was in receipt of any pension or allowance from Government or public funds e.g. Civil Service, Naval Base, Armed Forces etc.. This will be required so that the Registrar can forward a copy of the death certificate directly to these organisations. You do not have to do so.

What documents will I be issued with?

The Registrar will give you:

- A white certificate (form BD8 Rev) which you should use to tell Social Security about the death

- A Burial Order also known as the green form which the Funeral Director will need to arrange the funeral.

- If the death has been reported to the Coroner, the Coroner will usually inform you that the Burial or Cremation Order has already been issued. In this case you will not need to obtain it from the Registrar.

Is there a charge for registering a death?

No, there is no charge for registering a death. But you may need copy death certificates for informing banks, building societies, insurance companies, solicitor etc. There is a small charge for these copies. The Registrar will advise you of the current fee.

In respect of a stillborn child the process is slightly varied. The definition of a stillbirth is important as this will dictate how the process will occur. A stillborn child is legally defined as a child born after the 24th week of pregnancy who did not show any signs of life at any time after being born.

Stillbirth registration began on 1 July 1927 to help protect infant life. As well as being an important source of historical and statistical information, it also gives parents the opportunity to have their child officially acknowledged and to give him or her names if they wish to.

If a child is born alive, before or after the 24th week, and dies shortly afterwards then the event must be registered, but in a different way. Your Register Office will be able to advise you on this.

The stillbirth should be registered in the district in which it occurs. Registrations are by appointment to ensure that a Registrar is available, and an appointment can be made as soon as you have collected the medical certificate from the hospital, doctor or midwife as applicable. The stillbirth should be registered within 42 days and cannot be registered more than 3 months after it occurred. If no medical certificate is available because no medical professional was in attendance, then please contact the Register Office for advice.

There is also a facility to attend any other Register Office in England and Wales, which may be more convenient to you. This facility, called "registering by declaration" has the disadvantage in that certificates are posted to you within a few days rather than issued immediately.

Who can register a stillbirth and what will be recorded?

It all depends if the parents were married to each other at the time of the stillbirth or conception. If they were, then either the mother or father can go. If they weren't, who goes to the appointment will depend upon a number of factors:

- if you want the father's details to be entered in the register, then both parents can go and sign the stillbirth register together.

- if the father is unable to go to the register office with the mother, but you still want his details included, he can make a statutory declaration (on a form which we supply) in front of a Solicitor or Commissioner of Oaths, acknowledging his paternity, which the mother must give to the registrar. If the mother is unable to go to the register office with the father, she may make a statutory declaration acknowledging the father's paternity on the same form as above which the father must give to the registrar.

- If the father's particulars are not recorded in the stillbirth register, it may be possible for the stillbirth to be re-registered to include his details at a later date.

Although the majority of stillbirths are registered by parents, sometimes neither the mother nor the father are able to attend. In these exceptional cases, registration can still be done and the advice of the Register Office should be sought.

The details recorded are the date and place of the stillbirth, any name the parents' wish to give to the child, the sex and cause of stillbirth (where known – this is contained in the medical certificate issued to the parents). The name, occupation, birthplace and address of the parent(s) are also recorded.

What certificates will be issued?

Once the registration is complete, a certificate is issued to allow the funeral arrangements to be finalised. A Certificate of Registration is issued as proof that the registration has taken place and this is a legal document containing minimal personal information.

DUTY OF REGISTRAR TO REPORT DEATH TO CORONER IN CERTAIN CASES

By **Regulation 41(1)** of the **Registration of Births and Deaths Regulations 1987**, a Registrar who has been informed of the death of any person within twelve months of its occurrence must report the death to the Coroner in any of the following circumstances:

- where the deceased was not attended during his last illness by a registered medical practitioner

- if the Registrar has been unable to obtain a duly completed certificate of the cause of death

- where it appears to the Registrar from the particulars contained in such a certificate, or otherwise, that the deceased was not seen by the certifying medical practitioner either after death or within fourteen days before death

- where the cause of death appears to be unknown

- if the Registrar has reason to believe that the death was unnatural or caused by violence or neglect, or by abortion, or was attended by suspicious circumstances

- where it appears to the Registrar that the death occurred during an operation or before recovery from the effect of anaesthetic

- if it appears to the Registrar from the contents of any medical certificate that the death was due to industrial disease or industrial poisoning

Regulation 41(3) prohibits a Registrar from registering any death, which he has himself reported to the Coroner, or which he knows has been, or ought to be reported by any other person or authority, until the Registrar has received a Coroners certificate or a notification that the Coroner does not intend to hold an inquest.

Registration of death abroad

When a death occurs abroad, the appropriate civil registration procedure must be followed and this will then permit a death certificate to be issued.

However, such a death registration does not mean that the death is recorded in the United Kingdom. There is no legal obligation to register the death of a British national with the British authorities; nevertheless there are advantages in that, once registered, a British form of death certificate is available.

You can register the death with the nearest British Consulate if you live overseas or with the Consular services department in London, if you live in the UK. You can more information from the Foreign and Commonwealth Office website at

http://www.fco.gov.uk/en/travelling-and-living-overseas/births-marriages-deaths/registering-death

Consular death registration is not a legal requirement but there are some benefits:

- an entry will be made in the death register by the British Consulate in the country concerned

- you will be able to obtain a British format death certificate

- a record of the death will be held by the General Register Office in the UK

You will need to register the death with the foreign civil authorities and obtain a full foreign death certificate before you can apply for consular death registration. The consular death certificate will not include a cause of death as many foreign death certificates do not include this detail. If you are resident overseas you can apply for a consular death certificate from your nearest British embassy or consulate.

The Foreign and Commonwealth Office cannot register deaths which occurred in these countries:

- Australia
- Canada
- New Zealand
- Republic of Ireland
- South Africa
- UK Overseas Territories

The method of registration in these countries is similar to that of the UK.

From April 2010 the Foreign and Commonwealth Office will be able to start consular registering deaths which have occurred in the above countries except for the Overseas Territories.

It is often possible, when a death occurs whilst abroad, for the next of kin to liaise with the office of the High Commissioner when in a Commonwealth country or the Consul's office in other countries and for the death certificate and any other appropriate documentation to be presented to that Government official, who will instigate the initial inquiries for registration and issue the British death certificate which will be registered at the General Register Office in the U.K. Following the registration by the registering officer at either the High Commission or the Consulate, a return is made to the Registrar General. This return is made on an annual basis.

If the death has not been dealt with through the High Commission or Consulate in the country where it occurred, it is still possible for it to be registered in the consular register of deaths held by the British Embassy or the Consulate and for that record of death to be held, in due course, at the General Register Office.

If the death is to be registered in the appropriate consular register of deaths, then an application form must be completed and the registration officer must be satisfied as to the national status of the deceased. The following documents must be provided and should accompany the application.

- the civil death certificate issued by the local authorities;

- evidence of the deceased's claim to British nationality (a full birth certificate *or* of registration as a British national).

The Application form for Consular Death Registration requires details of the person whose death is to be registered, including:

- full name (and maiden name if appropriate) and sex;

- date and place of birth;

- date of death;

- address in full of usual residence at time of death;

- full address of place of death; and

- information about the informant (applicant).

The original documents must be sent – photocopies of documents are not acceptable – by recorded or special delivery mail. It is recommended that such documents are accompanied by a pre-paid recorded or special delivery envelope otherwise they will be returned by normal first class post. All documents are dealt with only through the post.

As the British Embassy or Consulate in the country where the death occurred will carry out the registration, it will therefore take approximately one month from receipt of the properly documented application before the consular death certificate is received.

Fees

For the current death registration fees please visit the following web address:

http://www.fco.gov.uk/en/travelling-and-living-overseas/births-marriages-deaths/registering-death

The information in this section was kindly provided by the Leicester City Council

Draft Changes to the Process of Death Certification

(England and Wales)

> Please note that the content of this chapter is based on work-in-progress and further changes may be made

Introduction

The *Shipman Inquiry's Third Report* published in 2003 stated that the existing arrangements for death certification, many of which have not changed since 1935, are confusing and provide inadequate safeguards for the public. The *Fundamental Review of Death Certification and the Coroner Service in England and Wales* chaired by Tom Luce came to a similar conclusion.

The Government's response to the Shipman Inquiry was set out in *Learning from Tragedy, Keeping Patients Safe*, published in February 2007. This was followed by publication of a *Consultation on Improving the Process of Death Certification* by the Department of Health in July 2007, and to the inclusion of relevant provisions in the Coroners & Justice Act 2009. The reforms set out in the Act are currently expected to be introduced from April 2012.

The provisions set out in the Act will simplify and strengthen the process for death certification in England and Wales by introducing a unified system for both burials and cremations and by appointing medical examiners to provide an independent scrutiny of the cause(s) of death stated by doctors on the medical certificate of cause of death (MCCD). This independent scrutiny will require a proportionate review of medical records and consideration of the circumstances leading to the death. Where appropriate, it will also make use of data to identify unusual patterns and trends and of concerns highlighted through clinical governance.

The appointment of medical examiners will have a significant effect on the current system because they will:

- replace the Secondary Certifiers who complete the current "Cremation 5" forms and the Medical Referees attached to crematoria who currently provide the final authorisation for cremations;

- improve the quality and accuracy of MCCDs and reduce unnecessary referrals to the coroner by providing advice and guidance to doctors;

- prepare MCCDs for deaths that do not need to be investigated by a coroner where the deceased person was not attended by a medical practitioner prior to death and which might otherwise require a post-mortem to enable registration of the death;

- ensure that bereaved people have an opportunity to provide information on circumstances leading to a death and are more easily able to raise concerns that might require a death to be investigated by a coroner; and

- provide information that strengthens local clinical governance systems and enables more accurate surveillance of public health.

The Government recognises that it needs to achieve these outcomes without imposing undue delays on bereaved families or unacceptable burdens on medical practitioners or others involved in the process. It also needs to ensure that the new system is transparent, proportionate, consistent and affordable.

The series of medical checks that are currently required before a cremation can take place cost families a total of £160.50. The effectiveness of these checks, which are not subject to robust quality assurance, were rightly criticised by the Shipman Inquiry. The Government's preferred option for funding the new scrutiny process is a single fee for the certification of all deaths – irrespective of whether death is followed by burial or cremation. The Government expects the fee to be lower than the existing cremation fees, which it will replace. As cremations account for over 70% of disposals, most families will pay less under the improved process.

Medical examiners will be appointed by NHS Primary Care Trusts (PCTs) in England or Local Health Boards (LHBs) in Wales and these organisations will be required to make available sufficient funds and other resources to enable medical examiners to discharge their functions. Whilst medical examiners are expected to be accountable to their PCT / LHB for achieving expected standards or levels of performance (for example on timescales and engagement with bereaved families), they will be independent in the way they exercise their professional judgement as medical practitioners. This provision and other related provisions are considered critical to ensure that medical examiners are able to scrutinise the causes of death in a way that is both independent and seen to be independent.

The programme of work to design, pilot and implement the improvements is being led by the Department of Health with active support and input from a wide range of stakeholders. These include representatives from NHS organisations, the BMA, Royal College of Pathologists, Coroners' Society, Coroner's Officers Association, the funeral industry, bereavement services organisations, Ministry of Justice, General Register Office, Local Government Association and the devolved administrations.

Significant progress has been made since Department of Health initiated the Death Certification Programme at the beginning of 2008 to work with stakeholders to design the new process shown opposite and to prepare primary legislation. The Programme has also established five locality-based pilots and a national pilot focussing on faith communities to evaluate the proposed changes and to contribute to the development of secondary legislation. The pilots are being supported by simulation modelling to carry out volume testing and validate the programme's assumptions on throughput, timescales and resources under different scenarios. It is anticipated that further pilots and / or early adopter sites might be established ahead of the introduction of the new process.

The Improved Process of Death Certification

Death certification in England and Wales is part of a wider process that starts with verification of the fact of a death and ends either with confirmation that burial or cremation has taken place or with registration of a death following an inquest. This wider process involves doctors, nurses, healthcare staff, bereavement officers, coroners, coroner's officers, police, mortuary staff, funeral directors, registrars and staff at cemeteries and crematoria.

The changes to the process of death certification have been designed in collaboration with a wide range of stakeholders to take account of their impact on the whole system. The new system is illustrated and outlined below. This is necessarily a high-level summary – details will be published by the Department of Health following further consultation and preparation of secondary legislation.

We anticipate that there will be many changes that occur. What we have decided to do is to give a very brief summary of some of the issues. The following paragraphs provide an overview of the new process of death certification and the wider process of which it is an integral part. Areas in which changes are being made are set out under individual headings.

Overview of Process for Death Certification *(from April 2012)*

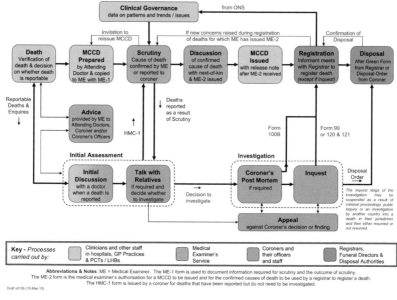

Please note that this content is based on work-in-progress and is subject to revision

Verification of the Fact of Death

When a person dies, the fact of death needs to be verified by a doctor or, where an appropriate local protocol is in place, by a suitably qualified and trained clinician or paramedic. If verification is managed well, it makes death certification easier and quicker to complete and ensures that safeguards are in place from the outset. We anticipate that there may be wider use of local protocols enabling better information on circumstances and concerns for death certification.

Decision on whether to report a death

When the doctor who attended the deceased person prior to death is notified about the death, s/he will review information provided by the verifier together with the deceased person's medical notes and patient records to decide whether the death needs to be reported to a coroner. We anticipate that Doctors' current practice to report deaths to the coroner becomes a statutory duty. Medical examiners are available to provide advice to doctors who are not certain about the cause of death. Coroner's officers and staff who receive calls from doctors seeking clarification on medical causes of death will be required to refer the doctor to a medical examiner.

Decision on whether the death needs to be investigated

When a coroner's office is notified of a reportable death a coroner's officer will carry out an initial assessment of the causes and circumstances to enable a coroner to decide whether the death needs to be investigated. This assessment will usually involve talking with the deceased person's attending doctor (or usual doctor) to identify a medical history and, where necessary, with next-of-kin or other people present at the death or associated with the deceased. If, following initial assessment, the coroner decides that the death does not need to be investigated, s/he will issue an HMC-1 form to the medical examiner stating that s/he has no further interest in the body and providing a copy of all the information used to reach this decision. At the same time, a coroner's officer will let the attending doctor know that a medical certificate of cause of death (MCCD) can be prepared. It is proposed that Medical examiners available to provide general medical advice to coroners and coroner's officers. Decision not to investigate notified to the medical examiner rather than to the registrar.

Preparation of a MCCD by an attending doctor

The attending doctor will prepare a MCCD and a release note and complete Part A of the ME1 for all deaths that do not need to be investigated by a coroner. Before preparing the MCCD and release note, the attending doctor will need to see, identify and externally examine the body of the deceased person. The original MCCD and release note must be retained securely and cannot be issued until the cause of death has been confirmed by a medical examiner. It is proposed that MCCDs will not be prepared for deaths that are reported to a coroner unless the coroner decides that they do not need to be investigated: this will remove the current problem of informants attempting to register deaths that are being investigated. The body of every deceased person will be seen, identified and externally examined after death. MCCDs will only be issued for use in registering a death after the certified cause(s) of death have been scrutinised and confirmed by a medical examiner.

Preparation for scrutiny

When a medical examiner's office receives a copy of the MCCD and ME1 (Part A) and appropriate medical records, it will review them to ensure they are complete and ready for scrutiny by a medical examiner. Additional medical records will be obtained where they are required and trends of previous deaths and any known areas of concern in relation to clinical governance will be highlighted. The proposed change aims to have a greater degree of detail. Preparation for scrutiny will be more robust than it is for many deaths in the current system. It will provide access to more information on individual deaths – both in terms of medical records and documented or unsolicited concerns raised by next-of-kin – and on how each death fits with patterns / trends of other deaths and with known areas of concern in relation to clinical governance. It will ensure that scrutiny no longer needs to rely on the knowledge and personal records of individual doctors to connect individual cases.

Scrutiny

Medical examiners will use information prepared and provided by their office to scrutinise each and all deaths that are not investigated by a coroner. It is proposed that Medical examiners will take over the work currently carried out by the secondary certifiers currently completing the "Cremation 5" form and medical referees attached to crematoria. Medical examiners will have specialist skills and expertise in scrutinising causes of death and will use an agreed national protocol to ensure that the scrutiny is robust, proportionate and consistent.

Clinical Governance

In scrutinising deaths, medical examiners will register and request investigation of health and social care issues that are evident from scrutiny of a death but are not, of themselves, sufficient to report the death to a coroner. It is hoped that scrutiny of causes of death and the quality of death certification will contribute to clinical governance in a stronger and more explicit manner. Medical examiners will work closely with medical directors and other senior clinicians and managers to identify any unusual patterns and trends in deaths. They will be supported in analysing data by staff working for Directors of Public Health.

Discussion of confirmed cause(s) of death with next-of-kin

The new process includes a specific requirement that a medical examiner, or someone acting on his / her behalf, discusses the confirmed cause of death with the informant who will register the death or some other person – usually the next-of-kin. The purpose of this conversation is to give this person an opportunity to raise any (new) concerns that might require the death to be reported to a coroner. The new process will ensure that next-of-kin etc have an opportunity to ask questions about the confirmed cause of death and to raise any concerns about this cause or the circumstances that contributed to it. This will address a key finding of the Shipman Inquiry that people who would have been able to provide relevant information about the deaths were not asked. It will also help make the process clearer to bereaved people – particularly those whose relatives die in a community setting or hospital where there is currently no centralised bereavement service to provide care and co-ordinate the process.

Confirmed MCCD issued for use in registering a death

When the ward staff, bereavement service or GP Practice staff receive a copy of the ME2 from a medical examiner's office, they will use it to 'confirm' the original MCCD and issue it to the next-of-kin together with the release note. It is anticipated that in most cases the ME2 will be received within 4 – 12 working hours of the copy of the MCCD and ME1 being submitted for scrutiny. A MCCD can only be issued and used to register a death and / or obtain a "Green Form" after the certified causes of death have been formally confirmed by a medical examiner. The period in which registration must be completed starts from the date of the medical examiner's confirmation, rather than date on which the MCCD was prepared. Information on implants, medical devices, infection hazards and applicant for disposal (currently included on cremation forms) will be included on a release note issued with the MCCD and provided by next-of-kin to funeral directors.

Investigation

Where the coroner has decided to investigate the death s/he will usually direct that a post-mortem be carried out and may decide (or be required by law) to proceed to an inquest. Coroners reforms set out in the Coroners and Justice Act have been developed alongside the changes to the process of death certification and care has being taken to ensure that both parts of the wider system support each other. It is proposed that a coroner's disposal order will be introduced and used for all deaths where the coroner starts an investigation.

Appeal

The coroners' reforms include the introduction of new process to appeal decisions made by a coroner. The medical examiner will also be able to use the appeals process in exceptional cases where s/he refers a death to a coroner who decides that it does not need to be investigated. It is proposed that the medical examiner will be an 'interested person' for the purpose of the new appeals process.

Registration

Before a registrar can register a death or issue a "Green Form" to authorise disposal, s/he will be required to check that the causes of death on the MCCD delivered by the informant have been confirmed by a medical examiner. It proposed that there will some changes in how these decisions will be reached. This activity will require comparison rather than validation of causes of death and will mean that registrars should not need to make sometimes-difficult decisions about medical issues or terminology. Registration will include an additional procedure in which the informant signs the reverse of the MCCD to provide evidence that the death certification process has been transparent.

Disposal

Final arrangements for burial and cremation will be made (or confirmed) after the funeral director (where one has been appointed) has received a copy of the registrar's "Green Form" (i.e. authorisation for disposal).

It is proposed that the current Cremation 1 form (previously "Cremation Form A") will be replaced by a form that is used for all deaths. Funeral directors will need to wait until they receive a release note after completion of scrutiny before they (or the undertakers) make any changes to the body of a deceased person that may render it unsuitable for a coroner's post-mortem.

The Coroner of England and Wales

Coroner's Office

Coroners are independent judicial officers in England and Wales who must follow laws which apply to Coroners and inquests. Each Coroner has a deputy and one of them must be available at all times to deal with matters relating to the inquests and post mortems.

The matters set out below apply only in England and Wales.

About 47% of all deaths are reported to coroners. Coroners inquire into many of the deaths reported to them, including all violent or unnatural deaths or sudden deaths of unknown cause.

If you wish to take the body abroad, you must give written notice to the Coroner. The Coroner will tell you within four days whether further enquiries are needed.

If you wish to bring the body back to England or Wales, the Coroner may need to be involved. In certain circumstances, an inquest may be necessary. You can ask for advice from your local Coroner's office.

Are all deaths reported to the Coroner?

In 2008 about 47% of deaths in England and Wales were reported to the coroner. In other cases, a GP or hospital doctor is able to certify the medical cause of death and the death can be registered by the Registrar of Births and Deaths in the usual way. Deaths must be reported to the Coroner in certain circumstances. Sometimes registrars or doctors may discuss the case with the coroner and the coroner may decide he or she does not need to investigate further, while in other cases the Coroner may ask a medical practitioner to carry out a post-mortem examination.

What is a Post Mortem examination?

A Coroner's post mortem is a medical examination of a body carried out for the Coroner by a medical practitioner of the Coroner's choice. Coroners will give notice of the need for a post mortem unless this is not practicable or would unduly delay the examination. The consent of the next-of-kin is not required for a Coroner's post mortem, but the next-of-kin are entitled to be represented at the examination by a doctor of their choice, if they have notified the Coroner of their desire to attend or be represented.

When can the funeral be held?

If the examination shows that the death was due to natural causes and that an inquest is not needed, the Coroner will release the body and you can register the death. The funeral can then take place.

If there is going to be an inquest, the Coroner can normally issue a burial order or cremation certificate after the post mortem is completed. If charges have been brought against somebody for causing the death, it may be necessary to have a second post mortem, and the release of the body and the funeral arrangements will be delayed.

Issue of the Death Certificate

If the death was due to natural causes, the Coroner will inform the Registrar and the death can be registered and a death certificate issued. In cases where there is going to be an inquest, the coroner can issue an interim certificate of the fact of death to assist in the administration of the estate. When the inquest is completed, the Coroner will notify the Registrar. A death certificate can then be obtained.

What is an inquest?

An inquest is an inquiry to establish who has died and how, when and where the death occurred. It is not a trial; the Coroner must not blame anyone for the death.

An inquest is usually opened primarily to record that a death has occurred and to identify the dead person. The inquest will then be adjourned until any police enquiries and the Coroner's investigations are completed. The full inquest can then be resumed.

Attendance at an inquest

When the Coroner has completed his or her investigations a date for the resumed inquest can be set and the people entitled to be notified will be told, if their details are known to the Coroner. Inquests are open to the public and journalists are usually present.

Witnesses called to give evidence

Coroners decide who should give evidence as a witness. Anyone who believes they may help, or believes that a particular witness should be called, should inform the Coroner.

Inquests with a Jury

The inquest will be held with a jury if the death occurs in prison or police custody, is believed to have resulted from an accident at work, or in some other circumstances. In jury inquest cases, the Coroner decides matters of law and the jury decides the verdict.

Inquest verdicts

Inquests do not determine blame and the verdict must not identify someone as having criminal or civil liability. Possible verdicts include:

- natural causes,
- accident,
- suicide,
- unlawful or lawful killing,
- industrial disease,
- open verdicts (where there is insufficient evidence for any other verdict),
- a narrative verdict, a short description of the circumstances of the death.

The Coroner may also report the death to any appropriate person or authority, if he or she believes that action is needed to prevent more deaths in similar circumstances.

Coroner's Certificate For Cremation

When releasing a body, a Coroner can issue a certificate for cremation.

Changes to coroner law

The Coroners and Justice Bill is currently going through Parliament (April 2009). The Bill will attempt to deliver more effective, transparent and responsive justice and coroner services for victims, witnesses, bereaved families and the wider public. The Bill includes many measures, some of the main ones being:

- create a new national coroner service, led by a new chief coroner

- create a new system of secondary certification of deaths that are not referred to the coroner, covering burials and cremations

The information in this section was kindly provided by the Ministry of Justice

The Police

Police investigations of sudden death

When a sudden death occurs, there may be a police investigation. The investigation will gather evidence to determine how the deceased died.

In the case of questionable death, a police officer will assist the Coroner.

In the case of a road traffic accident or major disaster, the immediate family may feel the need to visit the scene to make things clearer in their own mind. This can normally be arranged but, for reasons of safety, family members may be accompanied by a police officer and their appointed Family Liaison Officer.

Where a death is unexpected a police officer will attend the scene and will need to view the deceased to check for any signs that the death was not due to natural causes. This procedure is completed quickly and respectfully following which the police officer will complete a brief report for the coroner. The police officer will then arrange for the deceased to be taken to the hospital mortuary for the Coroner to decide on the next stage.

Where death is unexpected, a post mortem examination (sometimes called an autopsy) is held to determine the medical cause of death. This can only take place with the express permission of the Coroner and is usually carried out within three days of death occurring. The immediate family will be told that a post mortem examination is to be carried out.

A post mortem examination is carried out by a pathologist who supplies a detailed report concerning the cause of death to the Coroner. Some Coroners prefer the pathologist to give their report in person at an inquest.

The body of the deceased will normally be released for burial or cremation once the post mortem examination is complete. However, if there is an ongoing police investigation, this may be delayed.

In some circumstances, there may be a second post mortem (this can be requested by the defence in a criminal prosecution) which will further delay how soon the body can be released.

The Coroner and the police officers carrying out the investigation will be able to advise further on this matter.

The information in this section was kindly provided by the Leicestershire Constabulary

End of Life Care

The importance of good quality care at the End of Life has been recognised at a strategic level for some time, with establishment of the National Health Service End of Life Care Programme followed by the development of the End of Life Care Strategy by the Department of Health in 2008. The Department of Health Strategy uses the following definition for End of Life Care:

End of life Care is care that:

Helps all those with advanced, progressive, incurable illness to live as well as possible until they die. It enables the supportive and palliative care needs of both patient and family to be identified and met throughout the last phase of life and into bereavement. It includes management of pain and other symptoms and provision of psychological, social, spiritual and practical support.

National Council for Palliative Care 2006

The strategy acknowledges that in order to achieve the best outcomes, in terms of the quality of care given to people at this time Primary Care Trust's will need to work in partnership with Local Authorities and all those involved with care at the end of life. This should include partnership working both across the health and social care community and with voluntary and community organisations that represent the views of the communities in which they work. It challenges professionals to develop high quality services to meet the individual identified needs of those approaching the end of their lives, with the development of individual end of life care plans which set out the wishes of the individual around their care. A number of best practice tools have been developed to assist professionals in identifying those approaching the end of their life, assessing the needs of individuals and developing care plans to meet these needs. These include the Gold Standards Framework and the Liverpool Care Pathway, described below.

It is widely acknowledged that developing high quality End of Life Care is considerably challenging due to a number of reasons, including:

- As a society we do not talk openly about death and dying, often making it difficult to know what an individuals preferences are for the care they receive at this point in their life.

- People in the last stages of their life often need care for a number of services. This may result in them needing to or wishing to receive this care in a number of locations; for example home, hospital, care home and or a hospice. This requires an effective co-ordination of service delivery to ensure a smooth transition between services for the individual and their carer.

- Those approach the end of their life need access to care 24 hours a day, 7 days a week, something which services in the community are often unable to respond to. This can result in people being admitted into hospital as opposed to being cared for in the environment which they live.

- Each individual approach the end of their life differs in many ways depending on the nature of the condition form which they are suffering, social circumstances, spiritual/religious beliefs to name but a few. In turn this means that each individual's end of life care pathway will also need to be individual in order to meet the needs of the person.

The Department of Health End of Life Care Strategy sets out a number of key stages that are essential to ensure all individuals and their families experience high quality end of life care. These are:

Step 1 Discussions as the end of life approaches;

Step 2 Assessment, care planning and review;

Step 3 Coordination of care for individual patients;

Step 4 Delivery of high quality services in different settings;

Step 5 Care in the last days of life; and

Step 6 Care after death.

Alongside all of these steps attention also needs to be given to:

- Support for carers and families;
- Information for patients and families; and
- Spiritual care for patients and families.

It is widely acknowledge that effective communication will be a key element in ensuring the effective delivery of the strategy and as such the Department of Health requires Primary Care Trusts and Local Authorities to ensure that people working in this area receive appropriate training.

Alongside that strategy the Department of Health recommends a number of best practice tools that will assist practitioners in ensuring they are able to effectively identify those approach the end of their lives, effectively assess their individual needs and ensure that a high quality holistic service is given to meet these needs.

These include:

- The Gold Standards Framework

  A framework for care developed to ensure the delivery of 'gold standard' care to those approaching the end of life. It is best on a 3 step simple approach that requires practitioners to work with patients and their families to identify those that are in the last years of life, assess both the clinical and personal needs of the identified individuals and to plan care to meet these anticipated needs. The aim of the Gold Standards Service Framework is to develop care that is patient centred and encourages a collaborative approach to care between those professionals involved in supporting an individual.

- The Liverpool Care Pathway

  Is a programme of care aimed at supporting those approaching their last day and/or hours of life. Developed by the specialist palliative care team at the Royal Liverpool and Broadgreen University Hospitals NHS Trust, it is based upon an initial and ongoing assessment of an individuals care needs across four domains of care; physical, psychological, social and spiritual. The Liverpool Care Pathway provides guidance to practitioners on symptom control, comfort measure, medication, appropriate & inappropriate interventions, psychological/religious/spiritual care and care of the family. To ensure the effective delivery of the Liverpool Care Pathway in a new care setting a series of key steps are required:

    - Training of health and social care professionals;
    - Baseline reviews and analysis;
    - Implementation and reflective practice; and

- Audit and evaluation.

It is widely acknowledged that there is much to do to improve end of life care across the board however the development of the End of Life Care Strategy and the accompanying Quality markers give us the framework to drive forward change.

Further Information can be found from:

http://www.dh.gov.uk/en/Healthcare/IntegratedCare/Endoflifecare/DH_299

http://www.endoflifecare.nhs.uk/eolc/

http://www.goldstandardsframework.nhs.uk/

http://www.mcpcil.org.uk/

Disposal & Interment

Burial procedure (England and Wales)

Burial and Cemetery Authorities usually have their own Rules and
Regulations governing the management and use of their Burial Grounds
and Cemeteries. These will normally contain detailed provision as to the
following matters:

- The *time and place* for giving orders for interments and for the
payment of the required fees and charges.

- The *length of notice* to be given in the case of interments in graves
and vaults or bricked graves which are not already built but have to
be constructed.

- The *particulars* to be stated when an order for interment is given

- The necessity for *immediate written confirmation* of any order or
instruction given by telephone

- The production of the Registrar's *Certificate for Disposal*, i.e. the
certificate regarding the death issued by the Registrar of Births and
Deaths, or the *Coroner's Order for Burial.*

- The need for the relatives of the deceased to make their *own
arrangements* for the conduct of any burial service to be
performed.

- The *ordinary hours for burials* and the special and exceptional
provisions governing interments out of hours.

- The burial of persons dying of an infectious disease.

- The selection, excavation, preparation, marking and re-opening of
private graves. (Graves in which the Exclusive Right of Burial has
been or is being acquired).

- The *procedure* for obtaining permission to erect and inscribe a monument, memorial or gravestone, and the requirements as to their foundations, size, quality, erection and maintenance.

Registration of Burials in Cemeteries

All the burials in cemeteries provided under the **Local Government Act 1972** and **The Local Authorities Cemeteries Order 1977** must as soon as is reasonably practical after any burial in the cemetery, be registered in a book or books supplied by the Burial Authority concerned and kept by the officer or person appointed to that duty.

Cremation Procedure

The Cremation Regulations 2008 came into effect on 1 January 2009. They modernise and consolidate all previous regulations, replacing the Cremation Regulations 1930 as amended.

The appropriate guidance notes for applicants for cremation, funeral directors, cremation authorities and medical practitioners, together with related forms, can be found at web address

http://www.justice.gov.uk/guidance/cremation.htm

Under the Cremation Regulations 2008, applicants for cremation, or someone the applicant has appointed, have a new legal right to inspect the medical certificates that are produced for the purposes of cremation.

There are two medical forms. One is completed by the doctor who treated the deceased during his or her last illness, the other by a doctor who did not and who is independent of the first doctor. The second doctor has to examine the deceased, and discuss the death with the first doctor and at least one other person.

In short, no cremation can occur until the death has been properly registered and all relevant documents and certificates have been secured in accordance with the regulations.

The Medical Referee

Every cremation authority must have a medical referee who must be a registered medical practitioner. The general points relating to their role are as follows:

- Medical referees are unable to authorise a cremation unless the relevant forms have been properly completed in accordance with the regulations.

- Medical referees have the statutory power to reject incomplete forms and may refuse to authorise cremation until the forms are completed to their satisfaction.

- Medical referees also have the power to make any enquiry they may consider necessary about an application or certificate.

You should assist medical referees in the discharge of their duties by completing the cremation certificates fully and accurately, and by responding to any further enquiries as helpfully as possible.

Further information on can be found at the following websites:

http://www.direct.gov.uk/en/Governmentcitizensandrights/Death/index.htm

http://www.direct.gov.uk/en/Governmentcitizensandrights/Death/WhatToDoAfterADeath/index.htm

The information in this section was kindly provided by the Ministry of Justice

The Future of the Autopsy

No matter where you live in the world, there will be one or more systems related to the investigation of deaths of all types, be it a natural death in the community, a death whilst undergoing in patient medical treatment or a death related to trauma. These systems are country specific but most revolve around the answering of four basic questions; who the person was and when, where and by what means they came by their death. The investigation often involves an invasive autopsy but this is not the only method available to the authorities investigating the death.

Types of Autopsy Examination

Most members of the public will equate an *autopsy* with an invasive examination of the deceased body. However, there are a number of alternatives and variations of autopsies available throughout the world, which may fulfil the requirements of the investigators without the necessity for an invasive procedure. These are listed below. The availability of these systems is dependent upon where an individual dies.

Non-Invasive Examinations

There are only a limited number of truly non-invasive systems for death investigation. These are as follows:

View and Grant

The view and grant system is available within the whole of the United Kingdom and many other countries in the world. If a deceased person is referred for investigation then it is possible that this can be undertaken purely by a review of the available medical notes, consideration of the clinical history related to the circumstances surrounding the death and an external examination of the body only. If the doctor undertaking these procedures is satisfied as to the legal burden of proof required for that country, which is often *on the balance of probabilities*, that they can provide a cause of death and that there are no suspicious circumstances, then they can proceed with this and an invasive investigation will not be required. Although this practice is commonly associated with natural death, in some areas of the world unnatural deaths, such as suicidal hangings may also be dealt with in this manner.

Scan, View and Grant

In recent times, a variation of view and grant has emerged across the world which can be referred to as *scan, view and grant*. Added to the view and grant system is a non-invasive radiological investigation of the body (also referred to as a *near virtual autopsy*, or *Virtopsy^R*) usually with multi detector computed tomography (MDCT). By looking inside the body using a detailed radiological examination the investigator can, within the limitations of the technology, gain further support for their presumed diagnosis (see section below re MDCT and MRI).

Invasive Examinations

All other types of autopsies are invasive. They vary in the degree of invasive proceedure undertaken but all involve a breech of the skin. In all cases, the same clinical information and external examination components of 'view and grant' will be undertaken but these will be supported by an invasive investigation.

Needle Autopsies

There are a number of variants of needle autopsies including toxicological autopsies, fine needle aspiration and trochar biopsy autopsies. All of these use a variety of needle types and bore diameter to sample tissue or fluid from the body for the purpose of microscopic, toxicological or microbiological diagnosis. These can be undertaken in combination with MDCT examination.

Endoscopic and Laparoscopic Autopsies

The use of an endoscope, a flexible tube commonly used in clinical medicine to examine the oesophagus and stomach, or a laparoscope, a solid tube used clinically, for example to examine the abdomen, is practised in some areas of the world, such as Hong Kong. The body cavities can be examined with these instruments to a limited degree.

Partial and Limited Autopsies

The option to limit the autopsy to a single organ or body cavity is available, although technical difficulties in accessing the organ may result in a more extensive incision or examination than those requesting, or giving permission for, the procedure to be undertaken expected.

Full Invasive Autopsy

The final, and most common procedure, is the full invasive autopsy. This is considered by the medical profession as the gold standard examination and in many countries professional autopsy guidelines will require the investigator to undertake this full procedure. Deviation from this may have to be justified should the professional conduct of the doctor ever come into dispute. Thus although lethal pathology may be identified soon after commencing an autopsy, for example a ruptured heart attack or ruptured abdominal aortic aneurysm, a full autopsy may still be undertaken to satisfy professional regulations and guidelines.

Radiological Autopsies

In history the medical profession and lay community has questioned the need to undertake invasive autopsies although, until recent times, there has not been available a method to investigate the internal pathology present within the body without some form of invasive procedure. However, across the world, studies are now underway to consider the use of clinical diagnostic radiology in the form of MDCT and magnetic resonance imaging (MRI) as an alternative to the invasive autopsy.

MDCT is a type of x-ray where a rotating x-ray source travels down the length of the body with the resulting x-ray information being collected by a number of detectors mounted in the rotating scanner. This enables detailed 2- and 3-dimensional imaging of the body to be undertaken, from the surface inwards. The body of the deceased can be viewed using this system either on static or mobile scanners. MRI is similar to MDCT but uses a large magnet rather than x-rays to produce the images. Again deceased persons can be viewed with MRI

MDCT and MRI are diagnostic clinical devices designed for rapid, detailed examination of living persons. They were not originally designed to examine the dead. Thus, although both systems can be used with the dead, and, in fact, the detail of the examination is sometimes far greater than would occur with the living, for example in cases of bone trauma, the information that they provide has to be used in the context of the case. Both differ in the imaging they provide and both examine structures of the body to a differing degrees of clarity. MDCT is very good for bone trauma but for nervous system and brain examination one requires MRI for the best results. Ideally, both would be used, but in reality, only one, usually MBCT, may be accessible/available. In the case of MDCT it is also dependent on the number of detectors in the machine as to how much detail one can see.

To date, due to the development of the technology, MDCT, in the majority of cases, is an adjunct to an autopsy investigation but not a sole replacement. It can be used to provide a cause of death in the presence of certain types of lethal pathology and natural disease, for example, ruptured abdominal aortic aneurysm, heart attack and stroke. It can also be used for trauma. However, as with other forms of autopsy practice, it cannot provide microscopic or toxicological investigations and therefore one may miss a poisoning by using MDCT. However unless toxicology were undertaken at a conventional invasive autopsy then a poisoning may also be missed.

The problem with these technologies lies in the fact that the vast majority of people dying naturally die due to heart related problems. The argument is that as one cannot at present examine the coronary arteries in the same manner as one would at an invasive autopsy, one cannot use MDCT or MRI to replace an autopsy to diagnose a natural death. However the counter to this argument is that arrhythmia or early heart attack cannot be diagnosed by conventional invasive autopsy either and the diagnosis is based on a balance of probabilities on the basis of the failure to identify any other macroscopic pathology and the presence of narrowing of the blood vessels that supply oxygen to the heart.

The Future

At present, depending upon the circumstances of the death, in many countries including the UK, it is possible to investigate the death using a purely non-invasive system that is the 'view and grant' system. This can be supplemented by the use of MDCT. However, as technology develops and research can yet identify a reliable means of investigating the coronary arteries, then MDCT with or without MRI, may replace the invasive autopsy in many areas of death investigation.

Medical Issues

Doctors: Care for Dying Patients

It is established practice among healthcare professionals that the priority of care may not be a cure for a particular illness, but to alleviate suffering and improve quality of life. This secondary aim of medicine has gained prominence in the form of palliative care; with people surviving longer with fatal conditions, this area of speciality has developed rapidly. Dying nevertheless is a communal process – while the physical death occurs in an individual patient, the loss is felt by all those around him or her. In the biomedical model of illness, it is easy to overlook the physical and psychological impact of this process upon such people. In the age of holistic medicine, such aspects of illness need to be considered when a patient is dying, at the point of death, and thereafter. This section aims to highlight some of the challenges which may be faced in such circumstances.

The process of death and dying is difficult for patient, carer and health professional alike, and there can be conflicting expectations which may be wrongly interpreted by all parties concerned. The first of these can occur when identifying a dying patient and changing the focus of care. There can be a feeling from the patient and carers that the doctor or nurse has 'turned their back' or a sense of denial regarding the future prospect of a patient. Faith may or may not play a part in this. Partnership in making the decision of changing the focus of care should be a priority for the health professional. This may mean involving relevant family members or an interpreter if required. It may also take several consultations to reach a common understanding. Patients and carers should acknowledge that doctors and nurses are experts at identifying a dying patient, and should give their analysis serious consideration.

Most faiths attach special significance to death and dying – and it is important that this is considered when establishing priorities of care during the terminal phase. Initiatives such as the Liverpool Care Pathway have helped customise this care. Healthcare professionals traditionally feel comfortable dealing with physical symptoms, and are less aware of how to deal with non-physical complaints. It is therefore important that patients and their carers communicate their wishes clearly during this time. It may be that consciousness is more important than pain relief, for instance. Such issues highlight the subjectivity of the concept of 'quality of life'. The use of advanced directives and decisions regarding cardio-pulmonary resuscitation (CPR) should be taken during this period. A reminder to draft a will, if not already done, is also important. People of faith may be particularly opinionated on these matters so they should be given time to seek relevant guidance after the facts have been carefully explained to them, before a decision is made. CPR should be presented as a treatment option, like any other treatment, to be administered on the basis of clinical need and probability of success. The decision therefore is ultimately a clinical one, although patients and carers may be consulted in the process.

Followers of different faiths practice different traditions around the time of death, some of which may be considered essential to the wellbeing of the deceased or the grieving process of carers. Healthcare professionals should approach such matters with utmost sensitivity, particularly if the activities may need to be delayed, for example for a coroner's inquest.

After death, there can be a temptation for the health professional to 'get back to business as usual' and overlook the needs, grieving process and support of the carers. Their loss may be immeasurable and they may have forged a strong bond with the medical team whilst offering care for their loved one. They may appreciate a listening ear, insightful advice and a welfare call to check that they are coping. For some, the event is so overwhelming that they enter clinical depression. Losing contact with the medical team can exacerbate the problem. These people must be identified early and treated appropriately.

Death in Special Circumstances - Life-Prolonging Treatment

Technological advances such as artificial ventilation, haemodialysis and extra-corporeal membrane oxygenation have made it possible to sustain life in ways which were unthinkable in the past. Patients who have been ill enough to warrant such treatments may be in a state where their organs may be functional due to the assistance of machines but there is no other evidence of life. This has raised many moral, ethical and legal dilemmas reaching every level of society, as well as challenging religious perspectives on life, death and treatment.

Two central issues with regard to such scenarios include firstly defining death and secondly understanding treatments such as these in the correct context. These are complex issues for religious and non-religious minded people alike, and it is not possible to cover them within the scope of this book.

There has been much debate regarding definition of death. Currently the favoured definition for the medical profession is 'brainstem death'. This is where certain reflexes of the body, coordinated by the brainstem, are absent. This means that irrespective of the condition of the rest of the body, the brain has lost its core functions, and is not expected to recover. These can be assessed by qualified professionals, (usually an intensive care anaesthetist), when the need may arise, to clarify the matter. A typical situation is when a decision needs to be made to withdraw life-prolonging treatment such as ventilation. This can be a challenging decision to make for clinicians, and the experience can be distressing to relatives and carers. Religious guidance may help or hinder the process. One way to prevent this is by investing time in educating chaplains at hospital or religious ministers regarding such critical care issues, or inviting a nominated religious leader to a meeting to discuss a particular case. For clinicians, taking such steps where religious sensitivity is known about may save much more time spent in the courts to defend a decision.

Advanced treatments have carried with them an expectation from the public that all patients with critical illness qualify for them. As mentioned previously, all treatments are administered or stopped based on clinical grounds and included in this judgment is an assessment of whether a particular individual is likely to recover. Some people believe that by starting treatment with a ventilator, all relevant health problems will be solved. Health professionals and religious leaders need to eradicate this myth and explain that a ventilator is rarely a cure but more commonly a 'life-prolonging' measure to allow appropriate treatment of other potentially fatal disease. If there is limited chance of successful treatment, then commencing ventilation will not change this and may make matters worse. Patients with advanced heart failure, airways disease, cancer or multi-organ failure will in most cases be unable to survive independently of artificial ventilation once it is applied. This will then create the dilemma for the clinician: either leave the ventilator switched on with no hope of recovery, or turn it off leading inevitably to the death of the patient. Religious leaders should strive to understand the complexities of such issues when offering religious guidance to individual cases. The social dimension has not yet been mentioned. In brief, prolonging the life of a patient with a poor hope of recovery using artificial ventilation may deprive another patient with a good hope of recovery in an environment of limited resources. This may then lead to serious deterioration of health in the latter patient and even death. Even when religious teachings regarding the sanctity of life are upheld, it is difficult to justify prolonging one life on a ventilator when another is lost in the process. This is why understanding the context of life-prolonging treatment is essential to offer any meaningful religious, moral or ethical guidance on the subject.

Suicide and Euthanasia

Suicide is the deliberate death of an individual caused by his or her own actions. Assisted suicide is the deliberate death of an individual caused by the actions of a third party with the consent of the individual concerned. Euthanasia is the deliberate death of an individual caused by the actions of a third party, with the intention of ending their perceived suffering. All of these are currently illegal under UK law, with the latter two being synonymous with murder. Passive euthanasia is where death may result as a consequence of treatment given for a legitimate clinical indication (by administration of high-dose opioids in a cancer patient, for instance). This is currently permissible in UK law, however since the serial killings by Dr Harold Shipman – who exploited this grey area – the issue has become a highly sensitive one.

People who take their own life tend to fall into one of two main groups: those with mental illness such as depression or schizophrenia; and those with chronic (ie longstanding) or severe physical illness. A third group – where suicide is the result of ideological teachings with or without a religious basis will not be explored here since there is no medical context to this. At first glance, the two former categories seem very different. However, in both groups, there is a common sequence of events which may have a different source. In those with mental illness, social factors or mental symptoms lead to feelings of worthlessness, loss of hope and the sense that one's own life is not worth living. These move on to thoughts about suicide, with acts of self-harm which may precede a successful attempt on one's life. In those with physical illness, the loss of function and physical symptoms lead to similar feelings of worthlessness. Those with chronic illness may also have elements of depression. Speaking about one's own mood is a taboo issue to many people across different cultures, let alone voicing an opinion on the will to live. This leads to such feelings lingering for significant periods before presenting themselves to others and when known about, are not acted upon appropriately. If a suicide attempt is made or is successful, the ramifications in the family and community can be huge, and, due to the stigma, can be very negative. Preventing this situation is in everyone's best interest.

Health professionals and religious figures should educate themselves regarding the groups at risk of such illness and the signs to look out for. They should routinely ask about mood and feelings regarding life. They should become aware of local facilities in the public and voluntary sector that may be useful in such settings. If a person presents a significant risk to themselves, or there are doubts about their safety, the GP or out-of-hours primary care providers should be informed immediately. There may be a place for faith-based counselling in some settings, especially since they may help to build hope, establish limits, make sense of suffering and clarify the future for the individual concerned. Health professionals should also consider this option for their patients, especially when religion plays a significant part in their lives or when other treatments such as anti-depressants and standard counselling have not helped. In some cultures where the stigma of such feelings is greatest, individuals may not even realise that they are depressed or possess the vocabulary to articulate such feelings. They may instead complain of physical symptoms such as tiredness, sleeping problems and body aches and pains. This takes a lot of patience to deal with and skill to be able to recognise the possibility of depression.

Faith-based counselling can sometimes be entirely inappropriate and negative. This can be because the religious inclination of the one being counselled is not considered, or where the advice given fails to inspire hope and instead reinforces the stigma of vocalising such feelings, or, worse still, makes him or her feel more worthless. Those wishing to offer such counselling should seriously consider attending relevant training.

Preventing a suicide attempt is by far better than dealing with the consequences of one. Those close to the deceased are particularly affected, irrespective of their religious orientation. For such people, the process of grieving after a suicide is difficult because of feelings of failure in the duty of care and the consequential feelings of guilt and blame. Suicide cases must proceed to the coroner which may have a detrimental effect. Religious discourse regarding the one who commits suicide, which is generally very critical, can also be a factor. In some communities where stigma towards such events is prevalent, it can lead to isolation of individuals and families, thereby exacerbating the situation further. This may trigger further mental illness such as depression. Religious leaders and health professionals should be aware of such possibilities and be sensitive towards those who have to go through such a process.

Transplant Medicine - Organ Donation

Advances in medicine have made it possible to extract healthy organs in order to replace defective ones in other patients, thereby improving their quality of life and life expectancy. There are many patients on waiting lists to receive such transplanted organs. Most of them die before they receive one and so initiatives to boost the availability of organs are being developed.

Currently, anyone wishing to donate an organ has to make their preference known or join the organ donation register. The model of 'implied consent' where individuals have to opt-out of organ donation may replace this in future. There are many moral, ethical and legal challenges to the concept of organ donation alone and the issue of 'implied consent' has compounded this further. There is also increasing pressure for minority ethnic communities to be more fairly represented in the organ donation pool. This is because transplant surgeons look for the closest match of 'tissue types' (chemicals on the surfaces of organs which interact with the immune system) to minimise the risk of rejection. People who share a common ethnic background tend to be better matched.

Religious debates around the issue of organ donation include concepts of 'ownership' of the body and its components, purity of donated or received organs and desecration of the deceased. It is not possible to explore these in this chapter. However, it is important for those unfamiliar with the field to understand the basic facts of the treatments possible.

Live Transplant

This is where an organ is obtained from a living donor, where it is unlikely to cause deterioration in health of the donor. This may include donation of a kidney, where the other kidney is healthy and able to increase its activity to compensate for the loss. Bone marrow transplant and even blood donation can also fall into this category.

Cadaveric Transplant

This is where healthy organs are harvested from a deceased patient within a certain time frame. Organs transplanted in this way may include kidneys, liver, heart and lung.

Autologous Transplant

This is where a patient's own organs are used. A skin graft taken from one part of the body and put elsewhere is an example of this. Some patients undergoing intensive chemotherapy have bone marrow cells stored before commencing treatment. If the treatment leaves the patient without an immune system by destroying the remaining cells, the stored ones can be reinserted. The advantage with autologous treatment is that there is no potential for rejection, hence immunosuppressive drugs can be avoided.

Receiving a Transplant

Patients may need to fulfil certain criteria regarding their general health and specific illness before they may join the transplant waiting list. Assuming this is successful and a suitable match is found, they will need to have an operation to replace their faulty organ. Following receipt of a new organ in the operating theatre, powerful drugs called immunosuppressants need to be administered. These stop the immune system from mounting a response to the organ which it may recognise as a foreign object. It is a lifelong treatment. This leaves the body more prone to infections and cancers. In ideal situations, the dose of the immunosuppressant is reduced over time, the organ functions normally and serious infections and cancers are rare. Such patients experience a revolution in their health and can lead a near-normal quality of life. In practice, the drugs may be poorly tolerated, some transplanted organs may not function as well as initially hoped, some patients experience serious infections and cancers, and in others their body mounts an outright rejection of the donated organ.

Stem-Cell Research

This branch of transplant medicine uses stem cells (very young cells obtained from a developing fetus or umbilical cord) which have the potential to develop into any type of cell in the body, be it brain, kidney or heart for instance. This carries the prospect of generating a whole new range of cures for different conditions as well as using such cells to grow new organs in vitro for the purpose of transplantation. If a patient's own cells are used, the new organ would be an identical match and no drugs would need to be administered. This is also called 'cloning' and the cloning of an entire human being could theoretically also be possible. This has caused great controversy. At the moment, such techniques are highly experimental, but may be more of a realistic prospect in a few decades.

Post-Mortem Pathology Specimens

As well as offering organs for donation after death, individuals can opt to give up their body for scientific purposes. This may include use of the body for dissection to help teach anatomy to medical students, or to extract, preserve and display parts of the body, such as the heart or brain, for the same purpose. Scientific research may also include laboratory based experimentation on the obtained tissue. Similar moral debates surround this issue as with organ donation, such as duty of dignity to the deceased versus potential benefit to the life and health of others. The scandal at Alder Hey hospital where organs were taken from dead children without the knowledge of the parents has led to more restrictive measures put in place to prevent such violations from recurring.

Infection Control

Infections may pass from a deceased person on to others through contaminated bodily fluids. This includes blood, urine and faeces. It is therefore necessary to take certain precautions when handling the deceased. Disposable gloves and aprons should be used in all settings. Any open wounds in those handling the deceased should be covered with a plaster. Care must be taken to prevent such fluids gaining contact with the mouth, nose and eyes, therefore a protective mask and goggles may be appropriate in certain settings where there is a risk of this (for example when removing medical equipment which may be present in the body of the deceased). All those handling the deceased should wash their hands after contact. If there is high risk contact – ie such fluids fall into an open wound, the mouth, nose, eye or a 'needlestick' injury occurs then the area should be washed thoroughly and advice sought from appropriate emergency services.

The contents in this section was kindly provided by Dr Rashed Akhtar (Trustee - MBCOL)

Mass Fatalities – the challenges

Communities within the UK often face a number of serious risks which sometimes result in tragic consequences. These risks are many and varied and include events such as train derailments, chemical spillages, severe weather and building collapse.

We also face a very real threat from the rapid spread of contagious diseases such as pandemic influenza, which could result in the death of exceptionally large numbers of the population.

The role of the Local Resilience Forum is to support and co-ordinate the most effective response to these major emergency situations. A key aspect of dealing with communities that are affected by these events is to have a clear understanding of the religious and cultural issues surrounding the death of community members.

In order to deal with these issues in a sensitive and compassionate way, the Local Resilience Forum works very closely with faith and community leaders. However, it must be clearly understood that there will always be occasions where the needs of bereaved families cannot be met as quickly as might normally be expected. This particularly applies when a crime may have been committed which requires a lengthy and detailed investigation, or when bodies have become contaminated by chemicals or biological substances.

Fortunately these events are rare and for the most part the needs of the community regarding religious or cultural issues will be given the full respect that they deserve.

The contents in this section was kindly provided by Maureen Hepburn, Salvation Army. Alexis Wood, Leicester City Council

Wills

Introduction - Will and Probate

Key considerations that often arise following death are the affairs of the deceased and the deceased assets and liabilities.

Everything that a person has owned in terms of assets or liabilities are referred to in law as the estate and the estate needs to be dealt with promptly following death.

The various faith communities often have differing views on the manner in which the estate is dealt with and the way distribution occurs amongst beneficiaries, however it is important to understand the legal position in this area.

The positive advice from Lawyers and Probate Practitioners and even amongst members of the faith community is that every adult should make a will and review it on a regular basis, particularly if there are changes in circumstances.

General Terms

There are some very good reasons for making a will. They are as follows:

The principal reason why a will should be made is that the person making the will (the Testator) can make his or her decision as to who will benefit from the estate after his or her death. This will include any other gifts that the Testator may want to have in respect of specific religious obligations or charitable giving or donations to specific causes and also providing for specific individuals in his or her family. This becomes even more important when one considers the legal position in the absence of a will where the estate of the deceased is distributed and finalised in accordance with the Intestacy Rules.

The other reason that is often cited for a will to be prepared is in relation to financial liabilities such as Inheritance Tax. The law surrounding inheritance and the tax to be paid upon inheritance is regularly reviewed by the Government and financial limits are set from time to time. It is important that the whole issue of Inheritance Tax is studied carefully so that tax liabilities are minimised if the Testator wishes to bring maximum benefit to his beneficiaries.

If the Testator has young children or other persons who could be classified as vulnerable, such as family members with disabilities, then the will is a mechanism that allows the appointment of guardians to be responsible for such individuals. Such appointments are important and necessary and of particular importance to members of the faith communities who would wish their children to be brought up and taught within a specifically defined faith tradition.

The statistics are still extremely surprising in that the number of people actually making wills is still relatively low. Most people do not direct their minds to such issues because there are often negative feelings associated with planning for an event that most people choose not to think about. There is also reluctance on the part of some who consider the whole business of tax planning and the creation of wills as being too expensive.

The Will

A will in law is a legal instrument that sets out the specific wishes of the Testator and gives direction as to how his or her estate is to be divided amongst the beneficiaries and in what proportion.

In addition this document is also an opportunity for the Testator to give specific instructions the procedures to be followed in respect of the disposal of his or her body, together with the carrying out of any specific rites and other obligatory rituals, associated with specific faith groups.

It is also an opportunity for the Testator to write specific messages to the people he or she leaves behind.

A will is a dynamic document that triggers specific action upon death.

It is not surprising that most practitioners and lawyers will recommend people to make a will, as this gives an opportunity to determine and fix in law what they would wish to happen, not only to their assets, but also to their mortal bodies and also in relation to satisfying any specific or particular religious ritual, requirement and practice.

Intestacy Rule

Should a person die without leaving a valid will to deal with his estate the Intestacy Rules apply. These rules are fixed in law effectively deciding what is to happen in terms of the deceased estate. The operation of the Intestacy Rules mean that it does not matter what the Testator may have wished or wanted or promised whilst he or she was alive.

In general the Intestacy Rules will be applied in the following ways, although there are various permutations depending on each particular case. The various ways are set out below.

If there is a lawful spouse or Civil Partner to whom you are legally married, then if the estate is worth less than £125,000 (soon to be £250,000) the spouse will inherit everything. This is of significant importance to some faith communities where someone will "marry" another purely fulfilling the religious role, rites and obligations but will not formally go through an official marriage ceremony. In some faith communities there may be more than one spouse / Civil Partner and this can create some difficulties in the event that there is no will. There will be significant difficulties in polygamous marriages.

If the estate is worth more than £125,000 (soon to be £250,000) and the Testator has no other surviving relatives such as children or grand children or parents then the spouse will inherit everything.

If the Testator has a lawful spouse / Civil Partner and children and the estate is worth less than £125,000 then the spouse / Civil Partner will inherit everything. If the estate is worth more than £125,000 then the spouse / Civil Partner will receive £125,000 (soon to be £250,000) and a life interest (the right to take interest out of the remainder but not the capital itself) in half of anything over that sum. The children would get the remaining half sum that is over £125,000 (soon to be £250,000) immediately.

The above two examples are merely illustrations but the permutations and the way that the Intestacy Rules operate will often be contrary to what the Testator wanted and it is recommended that everyone should seek legal advice on the point.

Living "Wills"

Living "wills" are not wills as such. They are however key documents that deal with the whole issue of people having an illness, disease or prolonged medical treatment which threatens their life. This document dictates what should happen in the event that the person who has made the Living Will is under these circumstances.

There is evidence that these so called "Living Wills" can be described more accurately as documents that decide in advance what should happen in relation to stopping life prolonging treatment.

Living Wills are important in a situation where somebody is ill enough to require life prolonging treatment or procedures. In this scenario both lawyers and doctors often find themselves in a difficult position. Should the doctor follow the directions given to him by his or her patient in a Living Will?

We have also experienced advances in medical science and the advancement is such that there is now a much greater potential for individuals to be "kept alive" without any real prospect of such individuals being able to live independently at any time in the future. A Living Will therefore can deal with this extremely difficult situation.

There is still some doubt as to whether or not an incompetent or an unconscious patient, who has given specific statements applicable to these particular circumstances, creates a legally binding obligation upon doctors to follow these requests or continue life prolonging treatment.

At present the law is not settled but the general advice is that if a person is to make a Living Will it must be clear and concise and must consider what types of treatment that person would not wish to undergo.

General

It will be seen that the legal aspects of bereavement and death create many challenges. The crucial point is that those persons wishing to have specific matters dealt with upon their death, in terms of burial procedures and instructions or other methods of disposal of their body, and specific obligations required under their particular faith should seek legal advice and prepare a will and should also consider drawing up any other legal documents such as Living Wills or instructions to deal with any other issues that arise following death.

The Belief Groups

Baha'i

Definitions

The **Bahá'í** faith is one of the newest religions with an existence no more than 160 years old. Bahá'ís often introduce their faith through its principles, many of which appeal to people of other faiths, as well as people who are not especially religious. These include equality of men and women, harmony of science and religion, elimination of extremes of wealth and poverty and the establishment of a universal auxiliary language. The number nine is frequently associated with the Bahá'í faith: nine members of elected Bahá'í assemblies; nine Holy Days in the Bahá'í calendar; nine sides, approaches and entrances to Bahá'í Houses of Worship, representing openness, inclusion and universality. The nine-pointed star is a commonly accepted symbol of the Bahá'í faith.

Origins

In 1844, a young man known as the **Báb** or 'Gate' (1819-50 CE) began preparing the way for a great religious figure who would breathe new life into all humankind. The Báb's message caused uproar in his native Persia (modern-day Iran) where he – and thousands of his followers – were put to death. Some years later, a prominent Persian nobleman declared himself the one prophesied by the Báb. This was **Bahá'u'lláh** (1817-92) –whose name means the 'Glory of God' in Arabic. Stripped of rank and wealth, in the face of constant opposition, Bahá'u'lláh proclaimed his message of peace and unity for four decades. After Bahá'u'lláh's passing in 1892, his eldest son, **'Abdu'l-Bahá** (1844-1921) led the community, travelling extensively in the west to promote his father's teachings.

Beliefs

'Progressive revelation' is central to Bahá'u'lláh's teachings: the belief that knowledge of God has been revealed to humanity in stages by a succession of divine teachers, prophets and messengers. Bahá'ís accept Bahá'u'lláh as the 'Manifestation of God' to our times, in whom the attributes of God are revealed as fully as they can be in human form. Bahá'u'lláh embeds this new revelation within humankind's common spiritual heritage, describing it as the latest stage in 'the changeless faith of God, eternal in the past, eternal in the future.' Bahá'ís believe in life after death and in the eternal progress of the soul towards God. They believe in one God, the unity of the human family and the fundamental harmony of the world's faiths.

Scripture

During his 40 years of exile and imprisonment throughout the Middle East, Bahá'u'lláh wrote or dictated over 100 volumes on an amazing variety of issues. Many of these writings were addressed to the rulers of the world in his day. His best known work is a collection of short meditations called **The Hidden Words**. Bahá'u'lláh's writings, along with those of the Báb and 'Abdu'l-Bahá, constitute Bahá'í scripture. These texts were originally written in Arabic or Persian. Extracts have been translated into over 800 languages, including a considerable collection in English. Bahá'ís place great importance on everyone being able to read and understand these writings for themselves. They respect the scriptures of other religions, and often use them in their own study and devotions.

Worship, Prayer & Meditation

Adult Bahá'ís pray at least once a day, reciting one of three Obligatory Prayers written by Bahá'u'lláh: a short prayer, said between noon and sunset; one of medium length, said three times daily; or a long prayer, recited once in 24 hours. There are many other Bahá'í prayers, for all sorts of purposes, which can be adapted according to personal preference or local custom (e.g. chanted by solo voice or set to music and sung). Bahá'ís read something of their own choosing from their scripture every morning and evening. They believe it is better to read a short passage with feeling and understanding than it is to read for hours with none. Bahá'ís think of prayer as addressing God and see meditation as conversation with one's inner self.

Spirituality

To be true to their faith, Bahá'ís should live by their spiritual principles. They are encouraged to undertake work and studies that benefit the world at large and not to let academic achievement or material success make them conceited or become barriers between themselves and God. They see work performed in the spirit of service as worship. Bahá'ís have a personal duty to share their faith but are forbidden to try to convert anyone. They believe the best way to demonstrate religious faith is through personal example. 'Abdu'l-Bahá, who was described as 'walking the spiritual path with practical feet', once said, 'To be a Bahá'í simply means to love all the world; to love humanity and try to serve it; to work for universal peace and universal brotherhood.'

Lifestyle

Bahá'ís should not indulge in substances or behaviour which interfere with their rational faculties or compromises their personal dignity. They should avoid alcohol, non-prescribed drugs and backbiting. Smoking is discouraged, though not prohibited. There is no ban on eating meat. Bahá'ís may choose their own spouse but require parental consent before marrying. They are expected to refrain from sexual relations outside marriage. Bahá'í parents should raise their children as independent thinkers and world citizens, with the right to choose their own religion (or none) from the age of 15. Young Bahá'ís are encouraged to undertake a year of community service before embarking on adult life. Bahá'ís are free to dress as they wish but are advised to observe modesty. They are great believers in moderation.

Community

Anyone who accepts Bahá'u'lláh's claim to be the Manifestation of God and wants to practise his teachings is welcomed into the Bahá'í community. There is no initiation ceremony. The Bahá'í faith has no priests, ministers or clergy, no monks or nuns, no individuals in positions of authority. The community is guided by consultation and collective decision-making through a network of assemblies, elected at local, regional, national and international levels. Like other religions, there is variety of thought and practice within the Bahá'í community; but this has never caused a lasting split in the body of believers. The Bahá'í faith is funded by voluntary donations from its own members; they cannot solicit or accept financial support from anyone else for their own activities.

Festivals

There are nine Holy Days on which Bahá'ís should refrain from work or study. Most of these commemorate events in the lives of Bahá'u'lláh or the Báb. The most significant is the Festival of Ridván (21 April-2 May) recalling the occasion in 1863 when Bahá'u'lláh publically announced his station and mission. The first, ninth and twelfth days are particularly celebrated. Bahá'í Holy Days should not be given over to individual or collective sloth or indulgence, but be dedicated to charitable activities of lasting public benefit. Bahá'í New Year (**Naw Ruz**) falls on 21 March, ending 19 days of fasting during daylight hours for adult Bahá'ís in good health. Bahá'ís follow a solar calendar, so these Holy Days fall on the same dates each year.

Bahá'ís Worldwide

The Bahá'í Faith has more than seven million followers worldwide. The Bahá'í World Centre is located in northern Israel's twin cities of Haifa and Acre. The three central figures of the faith (Bahá'u'lláh, the Báb and 'Abdu'l-Bahá) are buried there, making it a place of pilgrimage. In 2008 these sites were named to UNESCO's World Heritage List in recognition for their 'outstanding universal value' to the common heritage of humanity. Each continent has a distinctive Bahá'í House of Worship, the most recognisable being the one in New Delhi, India. Popularly known as the Lotus Temple, it was dedicated to public worship in 1986. There are more Bahá'ís in India than any other country. The Bahá'í International Community has long held a respected position as a Non-Governmental Organisation (NGO) with the United Nations Organisation and other international bodies.

Bahá'ís in Britain

A vibrant British Bahá'í community has existed since the end of the 19th century. 'Abdu'l-Bahá visited Britain twice, in 1911 and again in 1912-13, to great public acclaim. A National Spiritual Assembly was established here in 1923, guiding the growth and development of the Bahá'í community ever since. Shoghi Effendi Rabbani (1897-1957), grandson of 'Abdu'l-Bahá, Guardian of the Bahá'í Faith from 1921 to 1957, is buried in London. Bahá'ís from all over the world visit his resting place to pay their respects. Since 1997 there have been Bahá'í Councils for England, Northern Ireland, Scotland and Wales. At the time of the 2001 Census, there were about 5,000 Bahá'ís in the UK, to be found in small but active communities, in almost a thousand localities the length and breadth of the country.

Death & Bereavement

What Happens After Death?

Bahá'ís have a very spiritual understanding of the human being. Although the soul is seen as immortal, they do not believe that it is reborn into another physical body, as in reincarnation. Rather after death an individual's soul develops and evolves through countless spiritual planes, whilst drawing nearer to God.

The soul then is able to grow and develop through one's relationship with God, which may be cultivated through prayer, knowledge, discipline and service to humanity.

Bahá'ís also believe in the concept of heaven and hell, but do not view this as a physical phenomenon, but a spiritual proximity to God. As the soul continues its spiritual journey even after death, heaven is looked upon as the soul getting closer to God and hell as a separation or distancing from Him.

As Death Approaches

There are no clergy in the Baha'i Faith, and every individual is expected to take responsibility for their own spirituality and its development. However this spirituality is usually enriched by reading the holy writings, service within the Baha'i community and the authority of an elected council called the 'Local Spiritual Assembly'.

It is this council that will often appoint a spiritual caregiver to visit, comfort and pray with and for a dying person. Unlike some other faith traditions the role of the spiritual caregiver is not to provide ministerial or priestly function, nor is it to act as an intercessor between them and God, but just like close friends and family, they are there to provide love, care and support at this difficult time.

Often they will remind the patient of the Baha'i teachings, the happiness they will experience in the next life and how to accept his or her transition to it. The carer may also provide similar spiritual support and understanding for family and friends.

The Moment of Death

At the time leading up to death, the patient will often wish to pray, they may ask for some assistance in this. It is common for friends and relatives to pray also, sometimes at the bedside or in a quiet place on their own. Some will pray quietly, whilst others may choose to chant. There are no set rules concerning what should or should not be done in this period, and much of what happens will be according to the wishes of the dying person and his/her loved ones.

Immediately After Death

Although the Baha'i Faith teaches that after death the soul has no further attachment to the physical body, the body must still be treated with dignity and respect as it was the temple of the soul.

Preparing the Body

With this in mind, the preparation of the body should be done with due care and attention. First it is gently washed and then it is wrapped in a shroud of white silk, cotton or linen. The deceased's relatives will usually decide who is to perform these rites. Some will choose to wash the body themselves, others will appoint funeral directors or allow hospital staff (male or female, regardless of the deceased's gender) to wash and wrap the body accordingly.

A Baha'i burial ring may be placed on the finger (this is a simple ring, inscribed in Arabic, translated as: 'I came forth from God, and return unto

Him, detached from all save Him, holding fast to His Name, the Merciful, the Compassionate ').

The body should be placed in a coffin made of hard fine wood and be buried with the feet pointing towards the Holy Land (towards the Shrine of Baha'u'llah (the Prophet-Founder of the Baha'i Faith), in Acre, in Northern Israel).

Method of Disposal

Bahai's believe that the body of the deceased must be buried as close to the place of death as possible. Ideally no more than an hour's drive from where he or she died. Although there is no obligation to bury the body within a set time after death, it should not be unnecessarily delayed.

Cremation is not permitted in the Baha'i faith. Neither should the body be embalmed, unless it is a requirement by civil law. Even then, the embalming process should not serve to prevent natural decomposition over a lengthy period. Likewise any means of speeding the process of natural decomposition should not be used.

The funeral service and burial arrangements are performed in consultation with family members or the local Baha'i community.

Funeral Procedures:

Baha'i funeral arrangements are deliberately kept simple and Bahá'ís's are requested to avoid any rigid rituals or fixed traditions. Everyone is welcome to attend the Baha'i ceremony, which is conducted with reverence and respect.

There are only really two basic requirements; that the body is buried less than an hour's drive from where he or she died, and that the 'Prayer for the dead' is recited, if the deceased was over fifteen years in age.

The recitation of this particular prayer which was revealed by Baha'u'llah, must take place before the coffin is lowered into the grave. This may be at a place where friends have gathered prior to the burial proceedings (sometimes at the service) or at the graveside itself. The entire prayer will be read out aloud by one individual from the Baha'i community, whilst the others stand and listen in silence.

The 'Prayer for the Dead'

This prayer is gender-specific, and so the wording is altered according to the sex of the deceased.

For Males:

O my God! This is Thy servant and the son of Thy servant who hath believed in Thee and in Thy signs, and set his face towards Thee, wholly detached from all except Thee. Thou art, verily, of those who show mercy the most merciful.

Deal with him, O Thou Who forgivest the sins of men and concealest their faults, as beseemeth the heaven of Thy bounty and the ocean of Thy grace. Grant him admission within the precincts of Thy transcendent mercy that was before the foundation of earth and heaven. There is no God but Thee, the Ever-Forgiving, the Most Generous.

For Females:

O my God! This is Thy handmaiden and the daughter of Thy handmaiden who hath believed in Thee and in Thy signs, and set her face towards Thee, wholly detached from all except Thee. Thou art, verily, of those who show mercy the most merciful.

Deal with her, O Thou Who forgivest the sins of men and concealest their faults, as beseemeth the heaven of Thy bounty and the ocean of Thy grace. Grant her admission within the precincts of Thy transcendent mercy that was before the foundation of earth and heaven. There is no God but Thee, the Ever-Forgiving, the Most Generous.

Followed by (for both males and females):

AlláhuAbhá [once]

We all, verily, worship God [19 times]

AlláhuAbhá [once]

We all, verily, bow down before God [19 times]

AlláhuAbhá [once]

We all, verily, are devoted unto God [19 times]

AlláhuAbhá [once]

We all, verily, give praise unto God [19 times]

AlláhuAbhá [once]

We all, verily, yield thanks unto God [19 times]

AlláhuAbhá [once]

We all, verily, are patient in God [19 times]

The remaining service and burial procedure is left to the discretion of the family.

Baha'is will often mark graves with a memorial or grave stone. Appropriate symbols for use on the grave stone are a nine-pointed star with the word 'Baha'i' in the centre, or the word 'Baha'i' on its own. Quotations from Baha'i sacred scripture may also be used on grave markers.

Mourning Practices:

Although it is understood that close friends and family members will need to grieve, and many will find the loss of their loved one very painful. The Baha'i faith teaches that death should actually be looked upon as a time of joy, as the soul has the opportunity to move on spiritually ever closer to its Lord.

Post-mortems and Organ transplants

Baha'is may donate their bodies or organs to medical science, indeed this is seen as a commendable act, but cannot be taken for granted, and is subject to the individual making this choice before they die. Post mortems are permitted if necessary, but provisions must be made to treat the body with care and dignity and ensure that any bodily remains are not discarded, but buried within one hour's travel from the place of death

We are grateful to Minou Cortazzi for her input towards this section

Buddhism

Definitions

There are many ways of defining a Buddhist. What they have in common is that they are inspired by the teachings and example of the Buddha, the 'Enlightened One', the title given to Siddahrtha Gautama (c560-483 BCE), the historical founder of Buddhism. Buddhism challenges some of the accepted Western ideas of what makes a religion; many people would rather describe it as a way of life or a practical philosophy, rather than call it a 'faith'. Buddhism is a path, which leads to liberation from the otherwise endless suffering of existence. The *Dharmacakra* (wheel of Dhamma) has long been recognised as a symbol for Buddhism. The wheel represents the cycle of life, death and rebirth; its spokes stand for the 'noble eightfold path', central to the teachings of the Buddha.

Origins

Siddhartha Gautama was born in what is today Nepal, where he was raised in the luxurious life of a prince. The story goes that when he managed to escape his palace and see the world as it really was, he saw, for the first time, a frail old man, a sick man, a dead body being carried for cremation and a wandering holy man. These sights were shocking to him, revealing essential truths about suffering, ageing, death and renunciation, leading him to abandon his old way of life. Having tried a number of traditional paths to liberation without success, Siddhartha Gautama famously became enlightened while sitting in contemplation under the Bodhi Tree. From his own experience, the Buddha established a practical system for helping others achieve a similar awakening.

Beliefs

Buddhists believe in an ultimate reality, but not in 'God', as most other religions do. They do not see the Buddha as a prophet, messenger, incarnation or manifestation of any such God, in the way that some other religions view their founding figures; indeed, the Buddha has been called the 'teacher of gods'. Buddhists see being born human as a unique opportunity for emancipation from *samsara*, the endless cycle of life, death and rebirth. Buddhists believe in the effect of *karma* (that deliberate action brings appropriate reward), that action depends upon state of mind, and that mind can be cultivated. At the end of the Buddhist path is *nirvana*, an indescribable blissful state beyond all normal human experience in which all suffering ends.

Scripture

Texts used by Buddhists fall into two main groups: those which are believed to be the words of the Buddha himself, and those of later scholars, commentators and holy figures following in the Buddha's way. The Buddha preached to his disciples, using parables and analogies, which were collected and written down after his death. These are called Sutra Pitaka (from the Sanskrit term meaning, 'basket of teachings') and are the core of Buddhist wisdom. In addition, the *Vinaya* covers monastic discipline, *Abhidharma* addresses philosophy, and interpretation is found in a huge quantity of commentaries. Outside the Buddhist community itself, the best-known piece of Buddhist scripture is probably the Lotus Sutra, a powerful and inspiring presentation of the universal influence of the Buddha's example and teachings.

Worship, Prayer & Meditation

The key act in a Buddhist's life is 'taking refuge'. Buddhists take refuge in the Three Jewels (or Triple Gem, as it is known in some traditions): the *Buddha* (the founder), the *Dharma* (the teaching) and the *Sangha* (the religious community). While they pay homage and respect the Buddha, Buddhists generally do not speak of 'worship'. The Buddha's statue and picture are often found in temples, shrines, centres and the homes of Buddhists as a focal point to recall his example. Silent meditation, inner contemplation, the making of offerings, chanting and prayer are among common practices of Buddhists of different traditions. Like any other tradition, in Buddhism, there is great diversity expressed in this aspect of individual and community life and practice.

Spirituality

In keeping with his practical approach to spiritual matters, the Buddha prescribed an Eightfold Path, encompassing wisdom, ethical conduct and mental development. This involves the individual practising right view, right thought, right speech, right action, right livelihood, right effort, right mindfulness and right concentration. These principles have proved adaptable throughout history and across cultures. Buddhist teaching also includes extensive description of ethics. In practice, Asian lay Buddhists may appear more 'devotional', whereas Western Buddhists could tend to maintain a reformed approach to Buddhist thought and 'spirituality'. An influential model for Buddhists is that of the Bodhisattva – an enlightened being who, out of compassion, delays personal entry into *nirvana*, to assist those still in this world.

Lifestyle

Buddhists try to live peacefully, following the Buddha's example and guidance, based especially in the Five Precepts (*Panchasila*). These are moral guidelines that Buddhists try and adapt to their personal circumstances: they should avoid taking life, harming any living thing, avoid taking that which is not given to them. avoid unworthy speech (such as lying, rumour-mongering, backbiting and gossip), avoid sexual misconduct and avoid contact with drugs and alcohol (since these cloud the mind and sound judgement). But the Buddhist lifestyle does not merely restrain its followers from doing things that they consider wrongful in body, speech or thought. It positively encourages daily *living* in simplicity, in which the individual expresses peace, gratitude, wisdom and compassion in whatever circumstances present them.

Community

There has always been great variety in how Buddhists see the Buddha's life, example and teachings, and huge diversity in how they have put his guidance into practice. Consequently, there are many different kinds of Buddhist communities, some concentrating on monastic orders, others operating in many cultural and social and projects involving both ordained and lay Buddhists. A 'cyber sangha' has begun to develop in recent years, exploiting the capacity of the internet to link those who are geographically separated. Buddhism is the one of the main religious traditions in the East, where it is common to see Buddhist temples, shrines, monks and statues frequently. It is also gaining more influence and followers in the West, partly due to increasing numbers of people practising meditation, and longing to find ways of more positive, practical and wholesome living.

Festivals

The Buddha discouraged placing any special significance on particular days. However, some festivals are celebrated by Buddhists, though they differ widely in form or specific date from one country to another. Most Buddhists will celebrate in some way, the birth, enlightenment and demise of the Buddha. South Asians do all these at the same time on Wesak, the day of the full moon in May. East Asian Buddhists mark the enlightenment of the Buddha in December and his death in February. In addition, each local Buddhist community is likely to have a number of festivals commemorating seasonal events and the anniversaries of particular sages and saints. Such celebrations will show great diversity, according to who is celebrating it, and where they are taking place.

Buddhists Worldwide

Estimates of the number of Buddhists worldwide vary, with an average of around 350 million, making up 6% of the global population. Buddhism has evolved into a number of distinct forms in different parts of Asia: Theravada (124 million followers) in Cambodia, Laos, Thailand, Sri Lanka and Burma; Mahayana (185 million) in most of China, Japan (where the well-known Zen form is practised), Korea, Taiwan, Singapore and Vietnam as well as in Chinese and Japanese communities within Indochina, Southeast Asia and the West; Vajrayana (20 million) in Tibet and surrounding areas in India, Bhutan, Mongolia, Nepal and the Russian Federation. Most Buddhist groups in the West are at least nominally affiliated to one of the three main Eastern traditions.

Buddhists in Britain

British interest in Buddhism started with the establishment of the Pali Text Society (1881 CE) and the appearance of various scholarly works. A couple of years before, Sir Edwin Arnold published his influential epic poem describing the life of the Buddha, *The Light of Asia*. Early British converts helped establish Buddhist missions in Britain, the first in 1908. In recent years, Buddhist organisations have presented Buddhism in ways suited to British enquirers. Buddhism is the sixth largest religion in Britain. At the time of the 2001 census, there were 144,453 Buddhists in Britain, making up hardly a third of 1% of the national population. There are currently thought to be around 250 Buddhist groups and centres throughout the country.

Death & Bereavement

What Happens After Death?

Buddhists regard death as an occasion of major religious significance, both for the deceased and for the living. For the deceased it marks the moment when transition begins to a new mode of existence within the cycle of births and deaths (*Samsara*). For the living it is a powerful reminder of the Buddha's teaching on the theory of impermanence (*Anicca*).

Buddhism considers the individual as being composed of psycho-physical combination of mental (perception, sensation, mental formations and consciousness) and physical (matter) aggregates. The dissolution of these two parts is called death and recombination of the two is called rebirth (*punarutpatti*). Buddhists view death as a natural part of existence. Even when a person is alive the cells in the human body are continuously dying and being replaced by new ones. Accordingly, for Buddhists, death and birth are taking place every moment, this specific view, the Buddha names as *khanika marana* instantaneous or momentary death. Hence the phenomenon of death is merely a more dramatic ending of this continual process. Death is viewed as a temporary end of a temporary phenomenon and not a complete annihilation; and so the concept of hell or heaven cannot exist. The end of this life paves the way to be born in another.

Buddhism accepts the idea of life after death, rebirth (*punarupatti*). But it is not a transmigration of a soul, or reincarnation (*punaravatara*) as explained in Hinduism, but the 're-becoming' or renewed existence (*punarbhava*) which is the Buddhist view of life after death. Buddhists believe that the karmic force remain undisturbed at the disintegration of the body, and resumes a fresh consciousness in another birth. The conditions of this new birth are determined by the conditions of the present birth and present *karma* (actions) combined with past *karma*. The present is the offspring of the past and becomes the parent of the future. This stream flows endlessly as long as it is fed by craving (*tanha*) and clinging (*upadana*) and ignorance (*moha*) until the self realisation of *Nibbana* (final Release). If one pursues to put an end to this cycle of births and deaths (*samsara*) then one needs to develop a sustained spiritual culture of moderation and constant disciplining of oneself in this life here and now.

Death for the Buddhist therefore is not the absolute end - but it does mean the breaking of all ties that bind one to its present existence. Therefore, the more detached one is from unwholesome conduct and its enticements, the more ready the one shall be when death comes.

Moment of Death

There are no taboos in Buddhism regarding the handling of a dead body, though it should be treated with dignity and respect. A dead body is neither to be feared nor unnecessarily clung to, as the 'being' has moved on. However, the final disposal of the body should be taken care of with the utmost dignity and respect.

Preparing the Body

When a loved one of a Buddhist family passes away, the body is commonly brought to the house for two or three days, whilst family members arrange for funeral rites and inform relatives and friends of the proceedings. The traditional Buddhist way in contrast, would have been to cremate or bury the dead body on the same day, reducing unnecessary financial expense or emotional grief for the bereaved family.

The corpse is first embalmed by the undertakers and then dressed (often in white to symbolise simplicity), before it is laid in a coffin. The price of the coffin may vary depending on what is affordable to the family. However, the price of a coffin and related paraphernalia has little to do with Buddhist doctrine and precepts. The Buddhist ideal is to make the procedure as simple and as easy as possible for the family that grieves a loss. There is no place in Buddhism for unnecessary expenses and meaningless customary practices and is much discouraged.

A room or a space is specially prepared to ensure that the coffin may be kept with respect and dignity in the family home. Family photographs if any on the walls are overturned. There are a number of different reasons given for this practice. But the commonly held view is to indicate that relatives and friends miss the deceased and that a period of mourning has commenced for the family. A single photograph of the deceased may be displayed beside the coffin. There may be various other local, regional, folk and even primal practices incorporated into funeral rituals, however they do not signify or convey the Buddhist teaching.

The body is placed in the coffin facing the West and sometimes a white canopy is hoisted which is seen as a mark of reverence. As the sun rises in the East and sets in West, the departure of the soul is likened to the sun setting.

Another common occurrence may be to light an oil lamp and keep it burning throughout the day and night, until the body is removed from the house. The lamp too conveys a deep vision about life, and the transient nature of all reality.

The Buddha taught four occurrences of death:

1. Death occurred by the exhaustion of life span.

2. Death occurred by the exhaustion of karmic energy.

3. Death occurred by simultaneous exhaustion of both life span and karmic energy.

4. Death occurred due to external circumstances, like accidents and untimely happenings.

The burning oil lamp symbolises the wick fading away in a similar style:

1. By burning down the wick in the lamp. This is similar to death through exhaustion of life span.

2. By the consumption of oil in the lamp. This is similar to death through exhaustion of karmic energy.

3. By the consumption of oil in the lamp and the burning down of the wick at the same time. This likened to the third mode of death.

4. By the affect of external factors, such as the wind blowing out the light. This is likened to the death occurred through external factors.

These rituals convey key Buddhist teachings and monks use such symbols to demonstrate to attendees, how to direct their thoughts on ethical living and to encourage them to emulate wholesome conduct in society.

Funeral Customs

Funeral rituals can be traced back to Indian customs, and it is presumed that most of the funeral rites of various Buddhist traditions have taken precedence over Buddha's own funeral ceremony. The cremation of the body of the Buddha and the subsequent distribution of his bodily relics are explained in *Mahaparinibbana Sutra*. (The discourse on great demise).

Buddhists may observe different funeral rites in different community or cultural settings. The main reason for this is due to the influence and intermingling of ancient customs, traditions, cultural strands and folk practices as Buddhism crossed to the rest of the world from the land of its origin. This exposition on Buddhist funeral rites is written here from the perspective of Theravada school of thought. Some funeral rites can very well embrace various customs of the locality in which the deceased has lived and incorporate the family customs which could easily be purely cultural or even primal.

Although there is no particular dress code at funerals, dress should be simple and modest, and sombre colours are preferred. (In Sri Lanka, people will traditionally wear white and this is regarded as a symbol of simplicity and solemnity). It is left to the individuals to decide exactly what is befitting for such an occasion.

What is common to all Buddhist countries is the concept of the memorial service prior to cremation or burial. Buddhist funerals are held with solemnity, in a simple ceremony but in a dignified manner. On the day of the funeral, Buddhist monks are invited to perform religious rites at the home of the deceased, a designated place or at the cemetery. The funeral proceedings are generally held in two parts. The first is the religious component and is performed by the monks, the second is what the close relatives perform just before the cremation/burial depending on which cultural background it's located across the Buddhist world.

The monks present at the ceremony commence the funeral proceedings by administering the five precepts. (to abstain from taking life, to abstain from taking what is not given, to abstain from sexual and sensuous misconduct, to abstain from false speech and to abstain from intoxicants which tend to cloud the mind: normally chanted in Pali but could be in other languages familiar to the devotees present). Observance of these five precepts is a moral reminder for those present at the ceremony of the importance of leading an ethical life which is the basic aim of Buddhist scheme of thought.

Next follows the ritual called '*mataka- vastra- puja*' – offering clothes on behalf of the dead. This white cloth which is offered to the monks is called '*pamsukula*' (literally a dust heap cloth).

The intention is to cut it in to pieces and then stitch it into a robe for the monks to use. This signifies how during the time of the Buddha, the monks prepared their robes. They would collect dirty clothes from cemeteries after burial rites. Then these were washed and cut into pieces, and stitched into robes to be worn by monks themselves. The offering of 'dust heap clothes' recalls the aforesaid story and symbolizes generosity of the relatives of the deceased that brings immense merit, which can be transferred to the departed one. After this offering, begins the chanting of a well known contemplative verse in chorus by all monks:

"Anicca vata sankhara uppadavayadhammino.

Uppajjitva nirujjanthi, tesam upassamo sukho." (Impermanent alas are formations, subject to rise and fall. Having arisen, they cease; their subsiding is bliss).

These three religious practices; observing of five precepts, offering of clothes on behalf of the deceased and listening or chanting of verses are all considered to be meritorious deeds.

Close relatives of the deceased may then sit together on a mat and pour water from a vessel to a cup which is placed within a plate until the cup overflows. This is done whilst reciting the following stanza three times, extracted from the Buddhist formula called, *"Thirokudda."*

"Idam me natinam hotu -sukhita hontu natayo"

May this merit be transferred to the deceased, may such be happy.

The pouring of water on to the hand or to the fingers of the relatives is a ritual used in most of the ancient cultures when bestowing something valuable officially. This Buddhist practice of pouring water into an empty vessel is a symbolic act, which denotes, that the living relatives have performed meritorious deeds in the name of the deceased and have transferred them to him/her, wishing a pleasurable existence in the next world. This ritual of pouring of water by the close relatives is performed in solemnity in the presence of the monks and the public witness this act in great reverence. It becomes in fact the last symbolic act of generosity of transference of all that the close relative can wish for the deceased. It is also a renewed act of solace and appeasement for the grieving relatives.

Then one of the monks will present an eulogy in the presence of the people gathered to pay respect to the deceased, but firstly directed to continue to console the grieving relatives, secondly to reiterate to the attendees the inevitability of death according to Buddha's teachings. Thus the monk talks further to remind everyone present to reflect on the nature of life and death, on impermanence and the need to lead exemplary lives doing good works when one is alive.

It is customary in certain ceremonies that once the religious service concludes some appointed persons present a number of condolatory speeches. These are presented normally by lay dignitaries and others, either connected to the deceased or those who have been close to the family of the deceased. All these help the grieving family to process their loss of the beloved. These conclude the formal proceedings of the funeral ceremony.

Method of Disposal

Buddhism has no set rule regarding cremation or burial of the deceased. The decision is often left to the next of kin, unless the deceased has expressed a preference. However, some Buddhists feel that as there is a scarcity of land and for hygienic reasons prefer cremation to burial. Even though Buddhism attaches no spiritual significance to the ashes after cremation of the body after death. Buddhists simply becomes an empty vessel of chemical elements and nothing more. It is encouraged to dispose of the ashes in any suitable way.

Mourning Practices

Grief is viewed as an unwholesome state of mind which should not be expressed in outward superfluous forms of mourning rather it is encouraged to transform this into an opportunity to reflect on the reality of our lives. Death serves as an invaluable reminder towards achieving an ethical form of living in order to reach ultimate bliss.

Buddhists believe that even after death, things may be done to add merit to a person's scale of deeds. This spiritual connection is strong among Buddhists and works well for the remaining relatives as a means to process their bereavement. The family and friends of the deceased offer *dana* (alms) to the monks on the third day and the seventh day, then on the third month and at the end of the first year and sometimes annually thereafter. Different cultures may observe these rites on slightly different days as Buddhism itself does not stipulate either the classification of dates or any specific rites.

The day after the funeral the monks are either invited to the house of the deceased or alms are brought to the monastery before noon. The alms and requisites such as robes, medicine and other requirements are offered to the *Sangha* (community of Buddhist monks), as a means to accumulate merit for the deceased. It is understood in Buddhist practice that to feed the monks is a meritorious act and to perform such in the name of the deceased helps the living to cope well with the sense of loss and process bereavement.

On the sixth night, a Buddhist monk is invited to the house of the deceased to deliver a sermon called *mataka bana*, (preaching for the benefit and in memory of the deceased). This hour long sermon will focus on the inevitability of death and the reality of existence, similar to the sermon delivered on the funeral day. This custom reiterates understanding that meritorious actions could be shared with the deceased (*pattanumodana*) and affirms its spiritual connection with the living.

At the end of these events, there is a sense of closure to the family mourning period, although this may vary slightly depending on national, regional and cultural practices of the Buddhist world. Some families continue ritually to commemorate the deceased annually. The key message in all these rites and rituals in the Buddhist scheme of thought is directed to the living and every death and a Buddhist funeral is a message to the living as to how they should live and behave in society.

Post-mortems and Organ Donations

There is no religious reason to object to the deceased undergoing a post-mortem in Buddhism, especially if the death has taken place in suspicious or unnatural circumstances and more investigations need to be carried out. Buddhist teaching is open that if the deceased has agreed that one's body be used for further investigations in view of conducive and appropriate medical advancements, then such be carried out with the full consent and the knowledge of the relatives of the deceased. In some cases post mortem is encouraged as if to reiterate the innate investigative nature of the Buddhist scheme of thought and the importance of the pursuit of truth as part of spiritual and ethical living.

According to Buddhist scriptures, the Buddha donated his body parts; eyes, flesh and blood, for the benefit of others on numerous occasions throughout his past lives. He sacrificed his whole self several times to save the lives of others during his own rigorous pursuit of attaining the Buddhahood. Therefore organ donation for the purpose of saving someone's life, helping them live a healthier life or for the enhancement of medical knowledge through the study of the anatomy, is viewed as a meritorious deed, emulates compassion and altruism in Buddhism. It also admonishes an incessant attachment or clinging to a body that decays and disintegrates.

We are grateful to Ven. Teldeniyaye Amitha, Dr.Shanthikumar Hettiarachchi & Susthama Kim who kindly provided the information in this section

Christianity

Definitions

Christians are people who have dedicated themselves to following the life and work of Jesus, also known as Christ (the 'Anointed One'). Christianity is the religion which has developed over the last 2,000 years from the personal example and divine teachings of Jesus Christ. Christianity is one of the Abrahamic faiths, along with Judaism (which comes before it historically) and Islam (which comes after). Church originally meant a community of Christian people but the word is also commonly used to signify a building where such a community worships. The cross is a universally recognised symbol of Christian faith. It is a reminder of Jesus' sacrifice, his victory over death and his resurrection. If Jesus' body is represented on the cross, then this is called a crucifix.

Origins

Jesus was born a Jew in the Middle Eastern town of Bethlehem some 2,000 years ago. Accounts of his birth and early years offer evidence that he was singled out to fulfil prophecy and do God's will. Jesus grew up in Nazareth, where he is believed to have been a carpenter. When he was around 30, he entered on his public mission, challenging the political oppressors and religious and social standards of his time, as well as healing the sick and performing miracles. After three years of this ministry, Jesus was arrested, tried and put to death by crucifixion. After three days God raised Jesus from the dead, and shortly thereafter his closest disciples were inspired to set out and teach in his name. These events are taken by many as marking the beginning of the Christian religion.

Beliefs

The Trinity is central to almost all Christian belief: God's nature is one and indivisible, though within that oneness exist Father, Son and Holy Spirit. There is variation in belief about the historical person of Jesus, though most Christians see him as the Incarnation of God – at one and the same time fully human and fully divine, free from sin. All Christians respect Mary, the mother of Jesus, although the Catholic and Orthodox churches do so to a much greater degree. There are differing beliefs among Christians about saints, angels and the problem of evil. Christians typically believe in life after death, although the condition attained by the individual soul is dependent on God's grace – salvation is a gift, and cannot be earned by anything human beings do in their earthly lives.

Scripture

The Bible as read by Christians is in two parts: the Old Testament (or the Hebrew Bible) is virtually identical to the central written scripture of Judaism. The New Testament presents Jesus' life and teaching (in the Gospels of Matthew, Mark, Luke and John) as well as the story of the community of Jesus' followers after his death and resurrection. The Apocrypha (certain books which are accepted by some, rejected by others) form part of the Catholic Bible, and are widely read by many other Christians too. Christians believe that the Bible addresses the most significant issues of existence in a way that is both timeless and contemporary. It is a source of inspiration and comfort, and is used for personal and communal worship and study by all sorts of Christians all over the world.

Worship, Prayer & Meditation

Christians worship in diverse ways, as individuals and communities: use of the Bible; music and singing; following a sermon; devotion to saints; expressing the inspirations of one's heart; silent inner contemplation;

confession and forgiveness of sins; prayer for others, living and dead; the taking of sacraments. The Anglican Book of Common Prayer describes the sacraments as 'an outward and visible sign of an inward and invisible grace', They are ceremonies or rituals from Christianity's earliest days, using material elements (e.g. bread, wine, water, oil) to convey spiritual blessings. The sacraments are indispensable to Orthodox and Catholic Christians, less so in other churches. Virtually all churches celebrate the Lord's Supper in some way, commemorating Christ's final meal with his disciples.

Spirituality

Christians believe that the Holy Spirit pervades all of life and creation, so it is possible to see spiritual content in everything. Even the worst excesses of human behaviour or the most inscrutable occurrences in the natural environment can offer important spiritual lessons. Because Christianity has influenced so much of human life and history for so long, it affects what can be seen as 'spiritual' in daily life, as well as in those moments that heighten our awareness of what it means to be human: music, the visual arts, sculpture, dance, architecture, philosophy, gardening, matters related to birth and death – all can be felt to express something above and beyond everyday experience, even for those who do not think of themselves as being particularly 'religious'.

Lifestyle

As far as they are able in their individual and community lives, Christians try to follow the example of Christ. This means doing what they think Jesus would do in everyday situations, particularly when they are faced with a moral dilemma. There is no scriptural or universally accepted prohibition on alcohol, drugs, gambling, eating meat or smoking, although some churches have worked out their own positions on these issues based on Biblical principles, as have many individual Christians. Paul (the most influential figure in the historical development of Christianity after Jesus himself) described the essential Christian virtues as 'faith, hope and love'. Paul's words summarise how a Christian should try to live, especially when he describes love as the greatest of these.

Community

The Christian community as a whole has four main groupings: Orthodox churches, their roots in the eastern part of the Roman Empire; Catholicism, dating from the western part of the Roman Empire, guided by the Pope; Protestant churches, developing from the 16th century Reformation onward, including Baptists, Methodists and Presbyterians (such as the Church of Scotland); Pentecostalism, which grew within Protestantism and includes many black-led churches. Anglicanism has some characteristics of the traditions and practices of both Catholicism and Protestantism. Words attributed to Jesus in St Matthew's Gospel show the significance of community to all Christians, no matter their particular church: 'Wherever two or three are gathered together in my name, there am I, in the midst of them.'

Festivals

The Christian calendar plays out the story of Jesus' life, death and resurrection across the year, though the dates on which these occasions are observed can vary considerably between different churches. The best known Christian festivals are Christmas Day (25 December in the Western Churches, 7 January in the Eastern Orthodox) which celebrates the birth of Jesus, and Easter (which falls at some point between late March and late April each year in the Western Churches, early April to early May in the Eastern Orthodox, following the cycle of the moon). Many non-religious cultural elements have become part of these long-standing holidays, and these occasions are now commonly celebrated by many people of other faiths or of none, as well as by Christians.

Christians worldwide

Over two millennia, Christianity has spread throughout the world, influencing life to some extent in virtually every part of the globe. The number of Christians worldwide is believed to be 2.1 billion, making it the world's largest religion, with 33% of the global population. Just over half these numbers are members of the Roman Catholic Church; there are 300 million members in Eastern Orthodox Churches, 77 million members of the Anglican Communion, and upwards of 78 million Pentecostalists. On the world scene, several nonconformist groups (e.g. Baptists, Methodists, Salvation Army and Quakers) have a notable presence. Other groups (such as Christian Scientists, Jehovah's Witnesses, Mormons and Unitarians) have distinctive stances on the life and teachings of Jesus that set them apart from mainstream Christianity.

Christians in Britain

Christianity is far and away the largest and longest established and most influential religion in Britain. It has had a presence here for over fifteen hundred years, and has been arguably the biggest single influence on shaping the legal structures, public institutions and social and intellectual traditions of the country. Some Christians today are anxious that their faith is becoming submerged in the diversity of religions and cultures; others are confident that it will prove adaptable and flexible enough to thrive. At the time of the 2001 census, there were just over 41 million Christians in Britain, making up almost 72% of the population. Only 8% of these people said they regularly attended church; 40% had never attended church, but still considered themselves Christian.

Death & Bereavement

What Happens After Death?

Christians believe that there is an afterlife, but they may vary considerably over what the nature of that afterlife is. The two main beliefs are:

That the human being has a soul which does not die, but which goes into the care of God upon death.

That the human being will die and will be raised on the Last Day or Judgement Day, when it will be decided whether they will go to heaven or hell.

The understanding of what heaven or hell actually are is again disputed. Some believe it is an actual physical phenomenon, whilst others believe that it is a state of mind: extreme happiness or eternal unhappiness. For both perspectives heaven is a place where ultimately you are close to God, and hell where you are distant from God.

The two broad beliefs about the afterlife are across the spectrum and depend on the interpretation of the scriptures. Many Christians would accept that the complete understanding of death is in the realm of mystery, a realm which cannot be fully understood in this life, but will become clear when a Christian dies, as only then will they know God as God knows them. There is a third position called Universalism, where believers cannot believe that a loving God would impose eternal punishment, but that everyone will ultimately be forgiven and cleansed of their sins.

Roman Catholics also believe that before one's final destination, there is an intermediary level called 'purgatory'. Here they will receive some punishment for the sins that they committed in life, hence 'purged of sin', before going on to Heaven or Paradise.

As Death Approaches

Although there are no particular requirements of where the patient should be as death approaches, the majority of deaths in England take place in hospital. That said, many patients these days would prefer to die at home, and a lot of effort is made (particularly by staff at hospices) to ensure that this happens. Attention is also given to ensure that relatives and close friends are present, whether at home or in hospital.

In the Roman Catholic Church particularly, there is the tradition of inviting the priest to pray with the person and to observe certain rites. The Hospital Chaplain often plays this role. However sometimes people wish to have a priest that they know well instead.

It is not necessary for the patient to do or say anything at this stage, however if they are compos mentis (of sound mind, memory and understanding), the priest will commonly exclude the relatives and ask the person to make a confession and give them absolution. This is not a requirement, but it is desired, and its purpose is to help a person cleanse their soul. Some believe that forgiveness is more effective if administered by a priest (in the name of Christ), but many others feel that as anyone may forgive another person's sins, it is not essential for a priest to take on this role. Over a period of time a tradition built around this, and people would feel very bad if the priest didn't get there on time. However the emphasis has changed in the current times, to focus much more on healing, and would have a particular relevance to people who are more seriously ill and those who are preparing for death.

In the Anglican Church and Roman Catholic Church, where possible, there is a 'Ministry at the Time of Death'. This is when the Minister/Priest, prepares the dying person for death, with a ritual including Holy Communion and anointing with oil, which may be administered by the Priest at this time.

Family and friends are not required to pray at this time, although many will and the priest will do this on their behalf. Often relatives value the farewell process and can also provide essential love and support necessary for the patient through this difficult period. Sometimes people may seek to be reconciled or seek forgiveness, so that a person may die in peace. This would therefore be recommended, as it has been known for a person to die in mental agony because they have unresolved issues on their mind.

The Moment of Death

Human sensitivity should always be kept in mind when a person is dying, to enable them to have as much comfort and ease as possible. Loud noise and unnecessary movement should be kept to a minimum. Small children are often excluded for this reason, so as not to disturb the dying person. However the objective is not to exclude children. In fact if a child is able to keep quiet some would regard it as good pastoral practice for them to see a person dying and to say goodbye. This may be traumatic, but is a basically healthy process which is often denied to children and difficult to sort out afterwards. The issue of children in peri-mortality situations is an important and live one and many believe that Western Christian tradition has been over-protective. Many Christians would therefore encourage children, especially those that were close to the deceased, to come to the funeral, (although there is no compulsion within the religion for this), but it may help them to cope with their loss.

It is useful for the priest or minister to remain present after death, to use prayers which have already been prepared to help people through the emotion and pain. If people wish to touch the body and say goodbye, there is no restriction, as long as they are sensitive to the family's needs. In some cultures there is occasional sensitivity towards women being involved during their monthly period, however most churches will steer away from any idea that women are in any way defiled by this natural process, and would strongly encourage them to attend the funeral.

Preparing the Body

The tradition of washing the body used to be undertaken by the female next of kin, at the home of the deceased. This is regardless of the deceased's gender. This seems to be an unwritten tradition. However in Britain these days very few people usually want to be involved in the preparation of the body for burial, and so in the majority of cases, the family will be happy for the undertaker to do it. There is a code of practice that Funeral Directors follow. This usually involves a partial embalming of the body (to prevent the body from deterioration) and a cosmetic element, which will involve presenting the body and the face so that it may be viewed by visiting relatives.

In some countries, the tradition of an early burial maybe preferred. The body might be kept in the person's home and then buried within two days. Hence there is little need for preparation of the body. Due to the cool weather in Britain, there isn't usually much degradation of the body and decay is held in check by the embalming and refrigeration process. It is thus more common in Britain for burial to take between 5 – 10 days after death. The wait is often necessary to ensure all friends and relatives are informed and able to get there for the funeral. The importance of this takes precedence over an early burial.

In both the Roman Catholic and Anglican Church traditions, the body is quite often brought into the Church the night before the burial or cremation, and there is a short service of prayer for the reception of the body. Otherwise, once prayers have been said after death, the body is taken away to the Funeral Director's chapel and the family and friends may visit at any time before the funeral.

Method of Disposal

There is no longer any real preference for burial or cremation amongst most Christians today. There is a shortage of burial space, and more people are choosing cremation.

There used to be a very negative approach to cremation up to about 50-60 years ago. This stemmed from an old set of beliefs derived from the religion itself, which teaches that on the Last Day at the General Resurrection, people will rise out of their graves. Belief was in a physical resurrection of the body, and therefore the body should be buried as it died. Many Christians today prefer to remain agnostic about this issue, and some feel that if God will raise the body to life, God will do this whether the body is mere bones or ash. In the New Testament, St Paul writes about the resurrection of the body, and explains that God's people will be clothed by God with a new body.

Although many Christian families still prefer burial over cremation and some branches of Christianity (e.g. the Eastern Orthodox Churches) forbid the body to be disposed of in any other way, cremation is still widely practised today. Part of the reason for this is because burial grounds are filling up. Respect demands that you consult the family before you re-use a grave and this cannot always be done. Also customs within the Christian tradition include the use of coffins of various woods. Some are lead lined or stone coffins and therefore not biodegradable, which means the re-use of grave space becomes more difficult.

Funeral Customs

It is highly desirable for friends, work colleagues and relatives to be at the service. Some families will take considerable pains to trace people in the deceased person's private address book.

Traditionally funerals would be public events and large sectors of the family's community might attend. In our more developed societies and large cities, community ties are not always as strong, and it tends to be only close family and friends attend. Some may even specify that the funeral is for family attendance only; this may be purely for practical reasons. However Christianity itself views funerals just as it does weddings, public functions that anyone is allowed to attend.

In most cases the body will be buried or cremated in the country where the person died. The Christian tradition does not encourage the deceased to be flown back to where they were born, except in the case of members of the armed forces. Similarly, this occurs quite frequently amongst the Irish community, where the body may be taken back to Ireland, especially if they have fewer family members in England. Those in service who have died abroad (such as missionaries) often choose to be buried there, thus underlining their commitment to the work.

Sometimes the deceased will leave information on how they want their funeral arrangements to be conducted; which hymns and prayers to recite and whether they wish to be buried or cremated. Depending on this decision the funeral will take place in either a church or a crematorium. Family and friends may wish to participate in the Lord's Prayer, the Word of God and Holy Communion.

A service of prayer is essential. In the Roman Catholic tradition a requiem mass is said, so that the main service of Christianity, the Holy Communion, Mass or Eucharist is offered at same time as the funeral takes place,. This is rarer in the Anglican tradition, and absent from the Protestant denominations, where there is a service of prayer, often with hymns and songs. Generally speaking, there are five elements which should be observed in holding the funeral service:

1. To secure the reverent disposal of the corpse.

2. To commend the deceased to the care of the heavenly Father.

3. To proclaim the glory of risen life in Christ here and hereafter.

4. To remind us of the certainty of our own coming of death and judgement.

5. To make plain the eternal unity of Christian people, living and departed, in the risen and ascended Christ.

Mourning Practices

In the Catholic tradition, rather more than in the Protestant tradition, there is the possibility of people requesting the priest to say the mass or Eucharist with the deceased person in mind for some unspecified period after the funeral. In some cases a record is kept of the day of the death of the person in a book on display in church, and there is a remembrance on the anniversary of the death on the nearest Sunday. A common prayer is:

'Rest eternal, grant unto them O Lord and let light perpetual shine upon them'.

Grief and the way it is handled is dependant on people's cultural influences rather than belonging to any church tradition. And therefore it would be handled differently by different communities. Some congregations may display more public crying, whilst others will be much more contained.

We are grateful to Rev. David Clark & Father John Lally for their input towards this section

Hinduism

Definitions

Hindus are people who practise the religion known as Hinduism, which they themselves call Sanatan Dharma. This means the 'Eternal Way to God' in Sanskrit. This way of living embraces many beliefs and practices, based on some broadly agreed principles about the nature and purpose of existence. 'Hindu' can also be used to describe one's cultural heritage and identity. This is not a religion of many Gods (as is often mistakenly thought). It is based on belief in one absolute cosmic energy, one God known as Brahman. The most sacred and commonly used religious symbol among Hindus is Aum. This represents unity with the essence of existence and is believed to be the fundamental vibration which created and sustains the universe.

Origins

Since Sanatan Dharma is eternal, there can be no single historical figure who may be described as its founder, and no particular date for its beginning. Scholars from East and West have traced its written history at least as far back as the civilization that flourished in the Indus Valley between 3500 and 1500 BCE. Hindus believe that the ancient scriptures of the Vedas ('knowledge') were heard by Rishis ('Vedic poets' or sages) in states of deep meditation and transcribed many years later. The religion known today as Hinduism has evolved in response to changing fortunes over 5,000 years, and continues to do so. Its chequered history helps account for its highly diverse, inclusive and accommodating character.

Beliefs

Hindus believe Brahman to be the one uncreated, unchanging reality behind the diversity of life, the source from which everything proceeds and the goal to which everything must eventually return. Brahman is expressed throughout the universe in an infinite variety of ways, some of them interpreted as 'gods' and 'goddesses', each with their own special qualities and functions. The goal of the individual soul (Atman) is to break free of the realm of illusion (maya) and gain reunion with Brahman. This is moksha (liberation). Those souls who have not yet attained liberation continue their search for God through the cycle of birth, life, death and rebirth (samsara), in various forms as dictated by the law of karma (cause and effect).

Scripture

Sanatan Dharma has many scriptures written in Sanskrit, which can be chanted and read. The Vedas are the oldest, dating in their written form from around 1500 BCE. The Vedas contain hymns, incantations and rituals, as well as scientific knowledge. The Upanishads (800-400 BCE) discuss the doctrine of karma and describe ways in which the soul can be united with Brahman. The Ramayana provides guidance for day-to-day living as a householder. One of the most popular scriptures (certainly the best known outside of India and the Hindu community itself) is the Bhagavad Gita ('Song of the Lord'), an extract from the epic poem, the Mahabharata, in which Lord Krishna instructs his disciple, Arjuna, about the requirements of the spiritual life.

Worship, Prayer & Meditation

Worship (puja) may take place in a temple (mandir) or at home in front of the family shrine, decorated with images (murtis) of gods and goddesses. Family background and personal preference influence which deities would be worshipped. By meditating on the divine attributes they represent, one is drawn toward a fuller understanding of the totality of Brahman. Many objects (e.g. candles, bells, incense, saffron water) appeal to different senses, drawing the whole person into the act of worship. There is no set day or time when one should attend temple; worshippers may be found there almost any time. Hindu temples in the West are normally devoted to many different aspects of God, rather than a single deity.   Purity and cleanliness are strictly observed in all acts of worship.

Spirituality

Hindus are encouraged to show love and respect for all creatures, as a way of recognising the presence of the divine in everything. Being accustomed to diversity of beliefs and practices within their own community, Hindus tend to appreciate the spiritual truths found in other religions. There is a very strong devotional strand in Hindu spirituality, called bhakti, in which individuals form a strong relationship with the qualities attributed to a particular god or goddess. This influences the way they express their personal spirituality in everyday life. Hindus will often follow a spiritual teacher (guru). Swamis (those who have learnt to master themselves) are adept at spiritual practices, and are sources of knowledge and guidance. To a Hindu, everything in life offers a spiritual lesson of some kind.

Lifestyle

Individual Hindus enjoy great flexibility in determining their personal values, and the best ways to put them into practice. So it is not uncommon to find committed Hindus, even in the same family, following different lifestyles. Hindus try to live according to dharma – righteous behaviour that brings one into step with the universe, expressed in a moral and ethical life. For example, most Hindus are vegetarian, arising from their belief in ahimsa (non-violence) in word, thought and deed. Similarly, most Hindus avoid alcohol and non-prescribed drugs. Some Hindus will fast or take vrats (vows) for purification at certain times of the year, or at certain stages of life. Hindus tend to be very supportive of charity, extending care and compassion to the wider community.

Community

Temples are focal points for the Hindu community, where they participate in a variety of events throughout the year. They are open virtually all the time, with various activities of a spiritual or social nature happening every day. Temples in this country serve a pivotal role in linking the Hindu community to external agencies. Differences between castes are not as rigid as they used to be, although the influence of the caste system can still be felt on the Hindu community worldwide. In India there is a thriving monastic and ascetic tradition, though this is not so prevalent among Hindus in the West. The concept of conversion is meaningless in relation to Sanatan Dharma. Hindus welcome anyone who wishes to follow and respect its universal principles.

Festivals

The festivals celebrated by Hindus mark seasonal, historical and mythological events, rites of passage, life events and family relationships, among other things. They all have underlying spiritual significance. Some are specific to certain regions, while others are celebrated by Hindus worldwide. Probably the best known is Diwali – a five-day festival when Hindus show particular devotion to Lakshmi, goddess of wealth and beauty. Diwali celebrates the triumphant return from exile of Lord Rama and his wife, Sita, as told in the Ramayana. Fireworks are set off to light their path home. Navratri is a nine-day festival during which Hindus worship different aspects of the great mother goddess, Shakti. Another popular festival is Janmasthami, which celebrates the birth of Lord Krishna.

Hindus worldwide

There are around 900 million Hindus in the world, making it the world's third largest religion, with 22% of the global population. Most live in India (780 million: 79% of the country's population), although there are sizeable Hindu communities in South-East Asia, East and South Africa, and other places where Hindus have migrated, such as the Caribbean. Outside India, the largest Sanskrit university for the theological study of Sanatan Dharma is in Germany. Many Hindu teachings have made their influence felt beyond the Hindu community itself, including various forms of yoga (from its use as a physical fitness and dietary regime to the diverse practices of meditation), vegetarianism, Ayurvedic medicine, and the social and political application of the principle of non-violence.

Hindus in Britain

Hindus had visited and worked in Britain for centuries before there was any notable migration here. The number of Hindu students and professionals in Britain increased markedly from the late 19th century onwards. In the 1950s and 60s, significant numbers settled here, some direct from India, others via African states such as Kenya, Tanzania, Uganda and Zambia. Most Hindus in Britain today are Gujarati (55-70%) or Punjabi (15-20%), the remainder being from other parts of India, West Bengal or Sri Lanka. At the time of the 2001 Census, there were 552,421 Hindus in Britain, 1% of the population. Hinduism is the third largest religion in Britain. There are over 160 Hindu places of worship around the country, some of which enjoy pilgrimage status.

Death & Bereavement

Hindu death rituals are drawn from The Vedas (Hindu sacred scripture). Some rites are traditionally carried out by a priest, but if there is no priest present they may be led by an experienced community member instead and performed by the chief mourner – often the oldest son, brother or husband followed by other relatives and friends.

What Happens After Death?

Hindus believe in reincarnation; that life is a journey and the soul of a human being lives multiple lifetimes, enters many bodies and reincarnates again and again until it is perfected, only then can it re-unite and become one with God in the state of bliss known as moksha.

Where the soul is reincarnated to, is very much dependent on its *karma* (action or deeds of that person). Thus a person's good intentions and actions will reap positive rewards and outcome, but a person's bad intentions and actions will result in suffering and misery. Karma is supposed to be self-regulating, in that the soul becomes more and more refined as it learns and develops this understanding of action and consequence. Hinduism thereby teaches responsibility in one's actions and behaviour, as only when moksha (a state of higher consciousness) is attained, can one be liberated from the cycle of rebirth and death.

As Death Approaches

If recovery appears unlikely, it is preferable for the dying person to be taken home, so that he or she may be amongst loved ones and in familiar surroundings. If this is not possible, the individual should lie in a room with their head facing North or East. They should be encouraged to chant a mantra (a religious syllable or poem, sometimes in Sanskrit). Loved ones will often recite prayers, hymns, and read scriptures also. A few drops of Ganga water and a leaf of Tulsi may be placed in the mouth at this time.

(Hindus believe that one should enter death in an alert state and so some may not be willing to take medicine when their time has come.)

The Moment of Death

At the time of death, as well as family and close friends being present, a Hindu priest may also be called to attend. A family member will chant the mantra softly in the right ear of the deceased. Then the following ritual may be carried out by the priest or a senior member of the family.

1) Holy ash or sandal paste is applied to the forehead,

2) Verses from the Vedas or Bhagawad Gita are chanted,

3) A few drops of Panchamrut (made of Milk, Honey, Sugar candy, Ghee, Yoghurt), Ganga (water from the Ganges River) or other holy water are trickled into the mouth.

Preparing the Body

The body is gently laid with the head in the South or West and feet North or East, preferably placed on the ground. This reflects the body's return to the Earth. It is also believed to aid in freeing the soul from the body. An oil lamp with a single wick, is placed near the right side of the head, and this is kept burning. The lamp is kept burning for thirteen days after death, near Lord Shiva's picture.

The dead body is viewed as impure, and so any physical contact is usually kept to a minimum. The eyes and mouth are closed. The hands are brought gently over the chest or by the side of the body. Relatives are encouraged to bid farewell and sing sacred songs or recite *Bhagavad Gita* (Hindu scriptures) at the side of the body. The body is taken away by the funeral directors and the date of the funeral is decided. The day before the funeral, the body is bathed. This may be carried out by family members of the same gender as the deceased. The body is dressed in new or favourite clothing of the deceased, then draped with a white cloth and placed in the coffin, with the face left uncovered. The coffin may be brought home for final farewell rituals and the coffin laid in the lounge.

The women present will offer *Khichadi* (cooked lentils and rice), near the body of the deceased as an indication of nourishment for the journey ahead. If the deceased was a married man, his wife will then place her bangles near the right hand of her husband, representing her enduring tie to him. The immediate family members go around the deceased four times offering flowers as they go around. Other family members may put flowers on the body, before the coffin is closed.

Method of Disposal

Hindus will usually cremate the deceased, although a few may prefer burial. Small infants will almost always be buried, rather than cremated. The funeral rites should be carried out by a male (next of kin) family member. A number of rituals will be performed at this point.

Funeral Customs

The crematorium provides a final opportunity to pray for the deceased's peaceful journey, as the soul departs from the physical body. Mantras and hymns are commonly recited or passages from the Bhagavad Gita may be read. One or two family members will pay their respect by recollecting sweet memories of the deceased to those present.

After the cremation a short prayer is said to Lord Shiva for the peace of the departed soul. All present will pray individually, donate to their prescribed charity and leave paying respect to the family by saying *Jay Shree Krishna.*

Family members may arrange to collect the ashes from the crematorium, at convenience. Often they will be sent to India to be deposited in the Ganges

River. Alternatively they may be placed in a nearby river or sea and bid farewell with flowers.

All family members in the presence of the deceased are advised to bath when they return home. This is mainly for hygiene purposes as they might have come into contact with the body of the deceased (even indirectly). During the ritual state of *Sutak,* (God given time to consider where life is leading and to try and learn from the experience. Be encouraged to prioritise one's purpose in life and make appropriate changes if necessary), they may not visit friends, attend festivals or go the temple (However friends and relatives may bring cooked food to them, to help them during their difficult period). Everyone present on the day of the funeral is usually requested to come and eat together at the home of the deceased or another chosen venue, at the end of the day.

Mourning Practices

Although grieving over a beloved one is acceptable in Hinduism, excessive lamentation is discouraged. Hindus believe that the deceased soul is extremely sensitive to emotional forces, and excessive mourning does not help it to move on. Instead, time should be spent in prayers, singing *Bhajans* (Hindu devotional songs, expressing love for the Divine) and reading scriptures. Also death should not be looked upon as a calamity, or viewed as the end, rather it is the natural progression of the soul which is immortal.

Hindus may hold several memorial services after the death of a dear one. Common dates for such memorials are on the 11th or 13th day after the death (or sometimes all 11 or 13 days). Rituals will vary significantly at this time, but usually, the final ritual service will be performed by the priest for the salvation of the departed soul. On this day relatives will gather for a meal of the deceased's favourite foods. A portion of food will then be offered to a photo of the deceased and later left at an abandoned place for the birds to eat.

After one month, prayers and bhajans may be held in the home of the deceased or a chosen venue and *Prashad* (food) may be served.

A yearly anniversary of the death (according to the lunar calendar) also takes place. Throughout these memorial services various rituals will take place, which may vary significantly according to people's own cultural and family customs.

Post-mortems and Organ Transplants

The Vedas and the Bhagavad Gita are very clear that the soul leaves the body taking with it all karma, and experience of life for the onward journey. Therefore, many Hindus will donate their organs as an act of good deed. Some Hindus may not feel comfortable donating their organs and so reserve the right to freedom of choice. For further information about this, local Hindu temples will be able to provide further advice.

We are grateful to Narandasbhai Adatia, Maganbhai Mashru, Hemang Bhatt, Rashmibhai Joshi, Ramanbhai Barbar & Rameshbhai Majithia for their input towards this section

Humanism

Humanists see our life on earth as our only life, and do not recognise any god or sacred books as having authority over humankind. The Humanist perspective is perhaps put most simply in the words of Tom Paine – 'my religion is to do good'.

You will hear many terms for the non-religious like atheist, agnostic, rationalist, freethinker, bright, secularist but these mean much the same and really represent different nuances or aspects of the same outlook. The term *humanist* is positive and emphasises the importance of what we all have in common – our humanity.

Humanists base morality on an analysis of the consequences of our words and deeds; on reason, intellect and shared human experience. The welfare of each individual, informed choice, happiness and sense of fulfilment are vital to defining purpose and value in life.

Humanists believe in the basic good in all human beings and strive to ensure that everyone - regardless of race, gender, ability or belief – is treated with respect. Human rights and individual freedom are important to Humanists, as is an understanding of difference.

Death and Bereavement

As Death Approaches

Whether, as death approaches, the individual is in hospital, at home or in any other circumstance, they will need to be comforted, secure and supported. Family and friends will need to be contacted.

During the lead-up to death, the individual may want to see a Humanist chaplain or non-religious pastoral visitor with whom they can talk about their concerns. Some hospitals now provide support within their chaplaincy teams from a volunteer Humanist chaplain.

Traditionally, people who choose to live without religion have not been considered to need the facility of a chaplain of a similar philosophy to their own, but the acknowledgement that this need exists is slowly being respected, although, unlike the religions, there are no paid humanist chaplains in the National Health service or in private practice. Religion must not be forced on the Humanist when life is ending – their outlook and philosophy on life must be respected.

There are no set rites or rituals that should happen at this point; any procedure will depend on the individual's wishes.

The Moment Of Death

If possible, the Humanist's loved ones will be with him/her, to provide love and comfort.

What happens after death?

For the Humanist, there is no separate soul or afterlife – life's journey simply comes to an end in death, but the deceased lives on in the memories of all who knew him/her.

What persists is the individual's works in the world, their genes if they had children, their influence on others, and the memories and love with which they are remembered.

The ashes or material remains of the body return through natural processes of decay to nature.

Preparing the body

In most cases an embalmer at the funeral directors will prepare the body. The deceased will be dressed in clothes chosen by their loved ones – or sometimes, before death, a person will express a preference for which clothes should be used. Sometimes relatives or friends will comb and arrange the deceased's hair. Often, loved ones lay mementoes like photographs, cuddly toys or flowers in the coffin to accompany the deceased. Although these are common practices they are not necessarily humanist – there are no specifically humanist formats for rituals.

Disposal of the body

Humanism does not require immediacy in disposing of the body. The procedure will mostly depend on the practicalities involved in arranging a burial or cremation with the appropriate authorities and close family. Delay may be unavoidable to allow mourners from distant places to attend.

Although many Humanists choose burial – usually in a public cemetery - the majority of Humanist funerals involve the less expensive cremation. Increasingly, people are deciding to arrange a 'green' burial in a natural burial ground for environmental reasons, whereas some own a family grave and will choose to be buried with other family members.

Cremated remains may be interred or scattered in a cemetery. Some people choose to scatter ashes at sea, on a mountain top, or at a place they loved to visit in life.

Funeral customs

As mentioned, there is no Humanist dogma to lay down ritual practices, and people vary widely in how they choose to say goodbye. A Humanist funeral ceremony might take place at the graveside – at a cemetery or natural burial ground. The funeral service could be celebrated at a crematorium chapel, a community centre, village hall or other public building, even one's home.

There is no requirement for the mourners to follow a special dress code. As far as possible, the wishes of the deceased and the closest relatives are central and their desire is most often for a joyous celebration of the deceased's life.

A typical ceremony will pay tribute to the deceased, outlining their life and character with respect, love, compassion, and sometimes with a little humour. Poetry, prose and favourite music – reflecting the deceased's personality - will be used where appropriate. The deceased will be honoured with dignity and warmth. Of course, no religious terminology will be used.

A Humanist celebrant will lead the ceremony; family and friends will sometimes also pay tribute during the service. Often, a photograph of the deceased will be displayed. Space will be set aside during the ceremony to remember the deceased in accordance with mourners' personal beliefs.

To assist the mourners in coming to terms with the loss of their loved one, committal words will symbolically commit the body to its end – back to the earth which sustains and regenerates all life. The Celebrant's final words will offer encouragement and inspiration to those who are left behind.

Post-mortems and organ transplants

If the authorities require a post-mortem, this will present no special problem to the Humanist.

Many people, although still not enough, consent for their organs and tissues to be used to help others – in transplants or medical research.   Some Humanists believe such consent should not be necessary – only the needs of the living should be considered.

We are grateful to Eleanor Davidson & Allan Hayes for their input towards this section

Islam

Definitions

A Muslim is someone who submits to the will of Allah (God), as it has been made known through the Qur'an ('Recitation') and the life of Muhammad, peace be upon him (pbuh) (570-632 CE). Muslims show respect for the prophet Muhammad, frequently adding 'Peace be upon Him' after saying or writing his name. These are the foundations of the religion of Islam (an Arabic word, meaning 'submission'). Islam is one of the Abrahamic faiths; its followers believe that it continues and fulfils the revelations of Judaismism and Christianity, both of which came before it. Like members of all other faith communities, Muslims practise their religion with varying degrees of observance and commitment. For some it provides a strong sense of national or cultural identity. The crescent moon and star is an internationally recognised Islamic symbol, which appears on the flags of several Muslim countries.

Origins

Muhammad (pbuh) was born in the Arabian Peninsula in the 6th century. Widely trusted and admired among the people of the city of Makkah, at the age of 40 he started to receive the word of God from the archangel Gabriel. When he made these revelations known, a group of believers began to gather around him, while others turned against him. In the face of increasingly fierce opposition stoked by the city's tribal leaders, Muhammad (pbuh) and his companions emigrated from Makkah to Madinah in 622. This event, called Hijrah ('Migration') marks the beginning of the Islamic calendar. After a decade of tests and trials, they returned to Makkah in triumph, firmly establishing their community there. Muhammad (pbuh) settled in Madinah, where he died in 632.

Beliefs

Muslims believe in one God, neither male nor female, with no children, parents or partner, and with whom none can be associated. This omniscient, omnipotent and omnipresent God was not created by anyone or anything, has always existed and always will exist, and rules over the universe with justice, mercy and compassion. At the core of a Muslim's faith is the declaration, 'There is none worthy of worship but God and Muhammad (pbuh) is His Messenger.' All Muslims believe this, as well as believing in the succession of prophets and messengers sent by God; in the existence and intervention of angels; in the Books sent by God; in the coming Day of Judgment and resurrection when the good and bad deeds of all those who have ever lived will be weighed.

Scripture

Muslims believe the Qur'an to be the word of God, revealed to Muhammad (pbuh) over a period of 23 years. Muhammad (pbuh) recited the verses as he received them, then taught them to his followers, who committed them to memory. Trusted scribes later wrote down the verses after rigorous cross-referencing and authentication by those who had memorised them. Great pains have been taken to ensure the purity of the text since that time. Muslims treat the Qur'an with reverence, in its printed form, or when hearing its verses recited aloud. Muslim children around the world are taught to read and recite it in the original Arabic in special classes. Most Muslims also look to stories from the life of Muhammad (pbuh) (Hadith) to help them follow his example.

Worship, Prayer & Meditation

Muslims are obliged to pray five times daily (dawn, midday, late afternoon, after sunset and late evening) out of love for God and obedience to His will. Muslims prepare for these prayers, which involve certain physical movements and must be said facing in the direction of Makkah, by ritual washing. Muslims are encouraged to offer all these prayers communally at a Mosque (Masjid) especially the Friday afternoon prayers. Sufism, a mystical devotional tradition which encourages a greater sense of union between the believer and God, has influenced much Muslim belief and practice over the centuries. It has inspired the work of many great poets, such as Rumi and Hafiz, many of whom are widely read outside the Muslim community.

Spirituality

Muslims do not see their religious duties as being separate from how they try to live in the world every day. They strive to observe those spiritual obligations known as the 'Five Pillars of Islam': Shahadah – the declaration of faith; Salah – the five daily prayers; Zakah – giving 2.5% of one's income to the poor and needy; Sawm – fasting during Ramadan (the ninth month of the Islamic calendar); Hajj – every adult Muslim who is physically, financially and legally able must make at least one pilgrimage to Makkah. Muslims show respect for the prophet Muhammad (pbuh), frequently adding 'Peace be upon Him' after saying or writing his name. They normally do the same for other prophets and messengers recognised in the Qur'an, such as Jesus and Moses.

Lifestyle

Given its long history and widespread acceptance, it is no surprise that there is variation in the ways Muslims practise their faith. For example, Muslims should dress modestly, but this varies according to the cultural background of the individual, family or community. Muslims only eat meat from certain animals, slaughtered using the halal method. Muslims are prohibited from eating pork or any foods product derived from the pig (e.g. lard). Islam also forbids any sort of intoxicant, such as alcohol or drugs. Shari'ah (Islamic law) is widely observed by Muslims in their personal lives, addressing such issues as marriage, family rights and inheritance.

Muslims should live according to God's command, but also obey the law of the land where they reside.

Community

A strong sense of community has been a vital aspect of Islamic life from its earliest days. Muslims use the word ummah to denote the whole community of believers, regardless of denomination or tradition, wherever in the world they may live, and at whatever time. Such lively and daily awareness of their kinship helps Muslims overcome differences between them, reinforcing their sense of unity around the world and throughout history. It motivates them to care for all those members of the ummah who may be less well-off than themselves, or who may be victims of misfortune – natural or man-made – in other parts of the world.

Festivals

The Islamic calendar is based on the phases of the moon, so dates advance by approximately 11 days each year compared to the Gregorian calendar. This means it is hard to predict the exact dates of Muslim festivals in advance.'Id al-Adha is the main Muslim festival, lasting three days, commemorating Abraham's willingness to sacrifice his son, Isma'il, as commanded by God. Muslims fast between dawn and sunset during the month of Ramadan. The holiest night in this month, Laylat al-Qadr ('The Night of Power') commemorates the revelation of the first verses of the Qur'an to the prophet Muhammad (pbuh). 'Id al-Fitr is celebrated at the end of Ramadan with three days of festivities, marked by acts of fellowship, peacemaking and charity.

Muslims worldwide

Islam is the second-largest religion in the world today, with Muslims making up more than a fifth of the world's population. Divisions that arose shortly after the passing of Muhammad (pbuh) have shaped the Muslim community over the centuries. The main groups which derived from this split are Sunni (the majority of the Muslim world) and Shi'ah (the largest numbers of which are in Iran, Iraq and the Lebanon). The vast majority of the world's Muslims are non-Arabs and do not speak Arabic; most now live in non-Muslim states; the country with the largest Muslim population is Indonesia. Muslim peoples have been able to retain the diversity of their own culture, while living with a sense of solidarity within a worldwide community.

Muslims in Britain

Middle Eastern and Indian Muslims – mostly seamen and traders – settled around British ports from the early 19th century onward. The first building dedicated to Muslim worship in Britain was in Cardiff in 1860; the first purpose-built Mosque was opened in Woking in 1889. After the First World War, many Muslims discharged from the British army settled here. Large numbers of Muslim workers from India and Pakistan were recruited for British industry in the 1950s and 60s. The 1970s saw further settlement from East Africa, then (more recently) refugees from Somalia and Bosnia. The 2001 Census records 1,546,626 Muslims in Britain – just under 3% of the population. Islam is Britain's second-largest religion. There are more than 700 purpose-built mosques around the country today.

Death & Bereavement

What Happens After Death?

Muslims believe that life in this world is only a short transitory state for human beings, and although it is important to live life to the full and make the most of every opportunity, it is only when they die, that the life of eternity begins, and they can finally meet with their Creator. The afterlife for a Muslims consists of a number of stages. There is a period in the grave, when the soul is believed to be questioned by angels. The space and conditions of the period in the grave will be subject to how one has lived their life. If a person has led a good and responsible life, the grave will be spacious and full of blessings, if otherwise it may be narrow and tight and not so pleasant.

Muslims also believe in the resurrection of the soul and the Day of Judgement. On this day every soul that has ever existed will rise before God and have his/her deeds in life presented before them. Depending on how they have lived their life, they may go to heaven or hell. These are real physical places for Muslims.

Muslims are always reminded to think and reflect upon the inevitability of death. Many verses in the Quran refer to the life hereafter, and remind Muslims to keep their actions and behaviour in check. As the life after is integral to how one lives their life now, it impacts on man's role on earth and the importance of his faith in relation to it. Being reminded of death, defines the purpose of a Muslim's life as a test, and Muslims believe that because human beings have free will, this understanding should encourage them to live a caring, responsible and useful life.

Muslims view life as a 'trust' from God and so have a responsibility to use it wisely and benefit those around them throughout it.

As Death Approaches

Muslims will often receive many visitors in hospital during this time. These could be friends or relatives, all wanting to spend some time with their loved one before they depart. They may also provide support and pray for them during this period, as well as remind them of the purpose of life and their blissful destination. Many with terminal illnesses may prefer to be at home during this time, so it is easier for people to visit, prayers to be said and the Quran to be recited loudly or quietly to support them.

As prayer is such an important aspect of Muslim life (adult Muslims are required to pray five times a day), many visitors may request the use of a prayer room or a place to pray. Although it is not essential, some hospital staff may change the direction of the patients bed, so it is towards the South East (direction of Makkah), and therefore easier for the patient to pray/ supplicate whilst sitting or lying down. This is a gesture of real kindness, not necessity, and is usually very much appreciated. It may also be helpful to have some copies of the Qur'an available for visitors to read or recite which is thought to provide a sense of peacefulness for the departing soul.

If there are members of the family or friends present at the time of death., they will encourage the dying person to pray and think of God, through *dhikr* (Quranic words, commanding the remembrance of God) and recite verses from the Quran. Family will also encourage the patient to repeat the *Shahada* the testimony of faith.

La illaha ill Allah

"There is no god, but Allah"

These should be the last words heard before death, and as Muslims are welcomed into the world with God's name, so they are bid farewell.

The presence of a religious leader is not essential at this time, especially if family and friends are present. If a Muslim chaplain is available, their support and assistance may be appreciated, and the patient and family should be informed of this service. Family members and friends may recite prayers aloud around the bed. Sins are not confessed to another person before death as Muslims believe that it is to God alone that one should repent. However, a dying person may wish to seek forgiveness from another person who they may have wronged.

The Moment of Death

The eyes of the deceased should be closed, and the lower jaw should be gently bound with a strip of cloth to the top of the head, to prevent the mouth from opening. The ankles should also be fastened together with a strip of cloth, to avoid the legs opening. The arms should be placed straight down the side of the body, with the finger straightened. The body should remain fully clothed, and wrapped in a sheet.

If family members are not present at this time, hospital staff should avoid touching the body of the deceased with bare hands. This is more to reassure the family that the body has been handled appropriately, rather than satisfy to any religious requirement. It is therefore preferable for staff to wear gloves when handling the body and, ideally to try to ensure that it is dealt with by a person of the same sex as the deceased. The body should be treated with the utmost respect, gentleness and decency and under no circumstances should the body be washed. Washing of the body is a very important duty for Muslims, which the deceased's family or members of the community are obliged to perform.

Preparing the Body

Bathing of the deceased is known as *ghusl,* and is looked upon as an act of great reward. Ghusl is an obligatory requirement. The foremost right of bathing the deceased belongs to his or her closest relatives, because this is their final deed of kindness for their beloved. Several people will be required for this process. An adult male should be bathed by his father, son or brother, and an adult female by her mother, daughter or sister. The more pious people in the community are usually approached to help, although any person of the same gender may assist in the process.

It is best for those washing the body to have performed the *wudhu* (ritual ablution/washing usually performed before prayer), before proceeding. Even in death, respect of a person's modesty must be upheld, and so the body is washed with gloves on and a sheet covering the private parts.

The body is dressed in a clean un-sewn white cloth *kafn* (shroud), which has been pre-cut and folded to the size of the deceased's body. (For more detailed information on bathing and dressing the body see 'Guidelines on death and burial of a Muslim, Muslim Burial Council of Leicestershire, MBCOL)

Once the body is dressed, it may be placed in a coffin (if one is being used), with the face exposed, to enable people to say their final farewells. The body may then be taken to the deceased's home or mosque for people to congregate and see them for one last time.

Funeral Customs

Muslims are required to perform the funeral prayer called *Salat-ul-Janazah*. Anyone can attend this and it is performed before the body is buried. Both the deceased and the people praying are seen to gain reward and benefit from this prayer.

The body is then taken from the mosque to the burial ground. Family, friends and community members will follow the funeral procession, and a final prayer is said at the grave, before the body is laid in its final resting place. The body is placed facing the direction of Makkah.

Method of Disposal

Muslims will always bury the deceased, never cremate, as soon as possible after death. It is believed that the deceased will want to return to the earth from which they came, as soon as possible, and any delay can cause considerable distress to the family. Ideally the body should be buried without a coffin. Some burial grounds in the country will allow for the body to be buried in this way. However if this is not possible, or a coffin is preferred, it should be inexpensive and made of a simple wood.

Although a Muslim grave may be marked, it should be done so in the simplest manner possible. The use of elaborate gravestones and decoration is discouraged.

Mourning Practices

The loss of family or friend is a deeply emotional and difficult time. This is wholly recognised and accepted in Islam, and every individual should be amply supported in their grief, as everyone deals with it differently. Public wailing or lamenting is discouraged though, and family should be consoled with the idea that the person has moved on to a better place, where one day they will be re-united with them.

Some of the information in this section was drawn from "Guidelines on Death and Burial of a Muslim", MBCOL September 2005

Jainism

Definitions

A Jain is someone who follows the teachings of the Jinas ('spiritual victors') a title given to a succession of 24 great teachers or Tirthankaras ('Fordmakers'), enlightened human beings who have shown the way to spiritual liberation since ancient times. The raised hand in the Jain symbol reminds us to stop and consider our actions. The wheel represents samsara (the endless cycle of reincarnation), the 24 spokes stand for the Tirthankaras and the word in the centre is ahimsa ('non-violence'). This is the supreme principle of Jainism and probably its best-known feature in the world at large. A Jain should avoid doing harm not just to people, but to animals, birds, fish and vegetation – even to the earth, air and water, down to the smallest of life forms.

Origins

Jainism has a strong claim to be the oldest living religion in the world, with no agreed date for its beginning. The most important figure in Jainism is Mahavira, whose name means 'Great Hero'. Latest in the long line of Tirthankaras, Mahavira lived in India in the 6th century BCE, at the same time as the Buddha. Like the Buddha, Mahavira rejected the prevailing wisdom that spiritual progress depended on correctly carrying out the duties of the class into which one was born. Mahavira taught that the only way for the individual to attain eternal bliss is to live in a state of discipline and renunciation, through right belief, right knowledge and right conduct. These 'three jewels' provide Jainism's path to liberation (moksha) and salvation.

Beliefs

Since Jains don't believe in an all-powerful God, the question of whether Mahavira (or any of the other Tirthankaras) is a prophet, messenger or incarnation of any such supreme being is a meaningless one. Jains see the eternal existence of the universe, without beginning or end in time or space, as self-evident, with no need of any creator to explain it. They believe that endless cycles of time stretch into the infinite past and into infinite future, and that the teachings which lead to liberation come in the form most suited to the present era. The time in which we live now is one of corruption and decay – including degradation of the natural environment – therefore a stricter form of discipline is required in order to escape from it.

Scripture

Mahavira's teachings were transmitted orally from teacher to pupil for generations before eventually being written down in the 4th century BCE. These were compiled into holy books called Agams, ranging in number from 33 to 45, depending on the Jain sect. Some cover specific topics, including Mahavira's final sermon, the environment and death. So Jainism does not have one central holy book, but many authoritative texts. One of the most revered books outside the Agams is the Kalpa Sutra, which tells the life stories of the Tirthankaras and codifies conduct for Jain monks and nuns. These texts are written in the ancient languages of Ardha-Magadhi and Prakrit. Nowadays, some extracts from Jain scripture have been translated into vernacular languages including Gujarati, Hindi and English.

Worship, prayer & meditation

Jains do not worship the Tirthankaras, but look upon them as living embodiments of perfection. Jains commonly chant mantras or contemplate images; such practices are known as puja. Recalling and reciting good deeds from the pious lives of the Tirthankaras generates a positive mental state in the individual, engendering religious merit which, in turn, contributes to good rebirth. Devotees focus on the Tirthankaras and other pure souls, so that they might follow their example more effectively. They may also engage in rituals involving decoration or anointing of images. Jains also practise a form of meditation called Samayika for sessions of 48 minutes, to establish a peaceful state of mind and obtain a flavour of what it means to follow a monastic life.

Spirituality

Jains believe that the souls of all living creatures are caught up in an endless cycle of birth, life, death and rebirth – and that it is the purpose of life to free oneself from this. Each soul is capable of achieving liberation when it rids itself of the burden of accumulated karma (the consequences of our deeds). This attaches itself to the soul and retards its progress toward the state of nirvana. This freedom is obtained by one's own efforts, under the guidance and direction of scripture and example. Jain spiritual insight and practice deal with the smallest aspects of daily life, as much as they address the big questions of the purpose of existence. Most Jains fast at special times, during festivals and on holy days.

Lifestyle

While the Jain way of life is rooted in ancient and traditional teachings, it is increasingly seen as being relevant to the needs of the modern world. For example, Jains should limit the extent to which they travel, and to which they consume resources. They should avoid violence, lying, lustfulness, and materialism, and steer clear of everyday sins, such as thinking or speaking badly of others, being inconsiderate or self-indulgent. Jains should also be charitable. Ahimsa directs the thoughts and actions of all Jains, as individuals and in their community (samaj). In keeping with this central principle, Jains are vegetarian. Some Jains show such commitment to their way of life that they choose to renounce all worldly things and become monks or nuns (though this is not so common outside India).

Community

Like most religions, Jainism has many branches or traditions, affecting its development throughout its history. There are two well-known denominations: Digambara ('sky-clad') – monks who wear no clothes and usually live in seclusion; Svetambara ('white-robed') who are more moderate in belief and lifestyle. While such divisions have long been influential to Jains in India, they are of less importance to those living in other countries today. Being in such a small minority in the UK, for example, has moved Jains to overcome many of these differences and build a robust community, for whom their common identity as Jains comes first. This unity is expressed in practical terms in Leicester's Jain temple, where all the main traditions have their own shrines or rooms for worship.

Festivals

Jains mark the passing of Mahavira and the ascent of his soul to nirvana in the festival of Vira-Nirvana (which occurs at the same time as the traditional Indian festival of Diwali). Paryushana is a festival lasting eight to ten days, during which the whole of the Kulpa Sutra is recited. On the fifth day of this recitation, the scriptures come to the birth of Mahavira – so Jains celebrate his birth on that day. During Paryushana, Jains get in touch with the original virtues of their soul. Its final day is a time of repentance. Jains celebrate Oli twice a year, for nine days each time. During this period, they eat bland food, once a day only. Jains follow a lunar calendar, so the dates of these festivals will change each year.

Jains worldwide

There are between 5 and 10 million Jains in the world, mostly in western and southern parts of India. Despite making up less than 1% of India's population, Jains have long had considerable influence on the religious, social, political and economic life of that country. Jainism was historically confined to India for many centuries, with no noticeable migration to the West until the late 1960s and early 70s, when many Gujarati Jains, who had previously settled in East Africa, migrated to Europe. Today there are thought to be around 25,000 Jains in Europe, with similar numbers in North

America. Many of these communities are now well established and confident enough to build their own places of worship, after Indian models.

Jains in Britain

At the time of the 2001 census, there were 15,000 Jains in England and Wales. Most of them live in London, Leicester, Manchester or Birmingham. Jains traditionally belong to the business community, although many Jains in Britain are professionals. There are four Jain temples in Britain: three in the Greater London area, one in Leicester. There are numerous Jain institutions, organizations and associations undertaking research and promoting community development. The Institute of Jainology (established at the first International Jain Conference in London in 1983) has become an authoritative source of information about Jainism. Young Jains UK encourages discussion of Jain philosophy, spirituality and its practical importance to the lives of young members of the Jain community in Britain.

Death & Bereavement

What Happens After Death?

Jainism propagates the 'Theory of *Karma* (Deeds)'. The basis of this is that all living beings have a soul; the soul can attract good or bad molecules, according to their good or bad deeds, known as *Punya* (Virtues) or *Paap* (Sin). The soul never dies but transmigrates to another body when it is time to leave the existing one. Thus when a body dies its soul takes birth in another form of living being.

The ultimate goal for the Jain is to attain liberation, *Niravana* and *Moksha* (these are all interchangeable words) and they mean to free oneself from the cycle of birth and death, otherwise known as transmigration - *Samsara*. Only at this point can an individual attain full knowledge of the universe and be at complete peace with oneself and existence.

If the soul is not yet at the stage of achieving Moksha / Niravana, it will transcend to another form, which could be within any of four categories; the animal kingdom, hell, heaven or as a human being. All of these realms are looked upon as actual physical states, in which the soul may have a different number of senses attributed to it. Accumulated Karma (Karma built up over one's lifetime) will affect which of the senses are attributed to it and which are not.

For example, it could be only the sense of touch that one is reincarnated with, which would mean the soul would only be able to enter the body of very small living entities in the earth, water, air, fire or vegetation. Alternatively if two, three or four senses are acquired, the reincarnated soul may reside in a particular insect or some types of animal. When five senses are attributed to the soul, it may enter other animals, humans, heavenly and hellish bodies. But only the human being's soul will have all five senses combined with the use of intellect. He alone then can exercise wisdom and judgment that enables him to escape the cycle of Samsara.

The ultimate goal of Moksha / Niravana, can only be attained through the human state. Only a human being has the faculties to reason, to judge right from wrong and decipher good from bad. Even the soul in heaven cannot attain Niravana before being human first, as it is still subject to transmigration, where as the premise of Niravana is a complete liberation from the cycle and to attain heavenly abode without having to be reborn again.

As Death Approaches

Ideally death would be at home, and if an individual has undergone a long-term illness and it appears that they are near the final stages of life, family may request that the patient be taken home to be with them. However when death is unpredictable, it is best just to accept wherever it is, and important to inform family and loved ones as soon as possible to be with them so that they can read religious texts or chant appropriate verses from the *canon* (religious teachings).

A good Jain ideally should not have any material attachment to physical assets or family and relations when death is certain. So that when a person is passing away, their only desire should be to seek forgiveness from their relatives, friends, and acquaintances for any wrong doing or harm caused during their lifetime, enabling them to focus their mind on the inner self. This sense of focus can be assisted by chanting particular verses from religious text, or if the patient is fully conscious, reading scriptural books written especially for this eventuality.

Although Jains do not have a formal priest, they do have lay preachers, who are similar to community priests, and would be useful if they are accessible to attend and assist the patient in seeking forgiveness, chanting mantras, hymns and prayers, and to help the dying person feel calm and at peace.

Next of kin and immediate family will usually contact the community priests themselves, through their own community contacts or links.

However, a Jain Chaplaincy service is currently being introduced into hospitals throughout the UK, to make it easier for patients to access help and support when such information is difficult to obtain.

The Moment of Death

Where possible it is always useful to have a *Divo* (a special light) lit nearby the dying person to create a sense of ambience, peace and tranquility for them. It is also a privilege to have use of *Vaaskshep* (a fine powder of sandal wood which has the blessings of learned gurus and monks). It is believed that this will help the dying person to move on to the next life in peace.

Preparing the Body

There is no strict formality on how to treat the body after death, apart from dealing with it with dignity and respect. Usually the deceased's family or members of the community will be involved in the washing and dressing of the body. This process does not have to be undertaken by a particular person, but whoever feels comfortable and has the emotional strength to help. Male bodies are prepared by males and female bodies by female.

Most people in the UK will use a funeral director to wash and prepare the body. They will liaise with the hospital or home directly to set appropriate dates at the crematorium. The body will be held at the funeral directors until the day of the funeral arrives. Only then will the washing and preparation of the body take place.

Traditionally, males are draped in white clothing and women are dressed in the traditional saree, but in Britain, men will usually be dressed in a suit. At the time of the funeral ceremony the body is covered with a white cloth or a shawl (over the clothes) for both the man and the woman.

Method of Disposal

The body is always cremated and not buried in Jainism, except in the case of small infants. It is preferred cremation be done as soon as possible after death. The Jain belief is that death is the end of life in that body, and the soul will have been reborn and moved on to another life immediately. As such, the body is like an empty vessel, and its ashes are of no real significance, so the Jain requirement is not to have the ashes taken away. (Though individual families may have other preferences).

Funeral Customs

It is very common to bring the body back to the deceased's home before the cremation process occurs. As well as an opportunity for family and friends to pay their respects, it is important that certain procedures and rituals are carried out at this point.

The funeral directors will usually arrange for the body to be brought back to the deceased's home. A white cloth is laid on the floor, and a swastik (holy religious symbol) of moong beans or a mixture of moong beans and rice is made on it, the coffin is then placed over this white cloth.

The prayers said during this period are very specific, although some people may vary some aspects of it depending on their own cultural influences. Although the majority of the Jain scriptures are written in Prakrit, prayers are mostly recited in Gujarati, with a Sanskrit influence. During the funeral, a general translation into English about the essence of prayer may be narrated to enable the younger generation to understand what is being said.

Five main prayers are used at time of death. They are primarily to provide peace for the departing soul and to ask for forgiveness on behalf of it. They are known as:

(i) *Jay karnara Jinvara*

(ii) Arhanto bhagvant

(iii) Khamemi save jiva

(iv) Sivamastu sarva jagat

(v) Antim Prathana – He naath jodi haath

Although there is no specific dress code for funerals, clothing for both men and women should be of modest appearance. Traditionally women would wear pale colours and avoid dark shades. Men, too, try to wear colours that do not attract too much attention.

Anyone may attend a Jain funeral and pay their respects to the deceased and their family. Usually, attendance will consist of family, friends, colleagues and associates. Most people will have been informed, soon after the death has occurred, by word of mouth, through a network of friends and family, which is sometimes known as 'passing of the message'. People are encouraged not to bring flowers to avoid violence to plants. Instead a donation box is available at the funeral. The money collected is donated to a charity of choice by the family.

There is also a practice of holding prayer meetings, and praying collectively for the departed soul. This will usually happen within a few days of the death, but before the funeral. Occasionally however, the prayer meeting is held after the funeral. People are informed of this event through a similar message system to that above.

During the prayer ceremony, as well as prayers being recited, it is common for a short presentation about the deceased to take place. Bereaved family will be consoled by members of the congregation, They, in turn, will give thanks to   all who attended the prayers. The family will also make donations to charities.

Mourning Practices

Jains view death as the body dying but the soul going on to live forever. So rather than sadness, there is an underlying notion of celebration, as the soul has moved on to potential liberation. However we all have emotions and a sense of attachment to those we love and the need for a period for grieving is understood. Jains believe that when the meaning of life and an insight into one's spiritual journey to attain such liberation are understood, the grieving process becomes easier.

Family and the community are often an essential means of support during this time. Between the time of death and the funeral day, friends and family will visit every day for an hour to provide support for the family and pray for the departed soul.

Post-mortems

Post-mortems are generally disliked by Jains. This is partly as the faith requires a sense of acceptance of what has happened, regardless of its cause, but mainly due to the delay it can cause to the funeral proceedings. Although this does not affect the release of the soul from the body (Jains believe that as soon as death occurs the soul moves on immediately, regardless of whether the funeral has occurred), any delay, such as a post-mortem can lead to bacterial growth from decay . This growth subsequently burns with the body thus causing violence to other living entities.

Organ Transplants

Jains believe that wherever you can help others, whether in life or death, you should. Hence there are no restrictions about using organs, but it is left to the individual's choice. The faith itself allows both giving and receiving organs.

We are grateful to Smita Shah for her input towards this section

Judaism

Definitions

Jews follow the religion of Judaism. There has long been debate over what being Jewish means. For example, from the Orthodox point of view, one has to be descended from a Jewish mother, or be a convert to Judaism, to be Jewish. However, the Reform movement also accepts those whose mother is not Jewish but who have a Jewish father. There are many people around the world who describe themselves as Jewish without being actively religious, as a way of defining their racial or cultural identity. If one has to distinguish between Jews and others, then those who are not Jews would be called Gentiles. The Star of David has been widely used as the most recognised symbol of Judaism since at least the 17th century CE.

Origins

The Jewish people have a long and dramatic history. Their religion has developed over a period of more than 4,000 years, going back to Abraham, who upheld what came to be the main principle of Judaism: monotheism, the belief that there is only one G_d. Jews believe that G_d made a covenant with Abraham, giving his descendants a special responsibility to keep his commandments. At a later time, G_d revealed his laws to Moses on Mount Sinai in the form of the Torah. The events of Jewish history and the doctrines of the religion have had a profound influence on Christianity, Islam and the Bahá'í Faith, monotheistic religions which arose later in history and locate their spiritual heritage within the Abrahamic tradition.

Beliefs

Judaism has developed under a great variety of circumstances throughout its long history, and in many different parts of the world. So it is no surprise that there is considerable variation in belief and practice amongst Jewish people. It could safely be said, that virtually all observant Jews, no matter their tradition, would accept the following: that G_d exists, eternal and without physical form; that G_d created the universe and continues to govern it; that G_d knows all thoughts and deeds; that G_d will reward the good and punish the wicked; and that G_d is the only one to whom prayer should be directed; that the prophets spoke truth; that Moses, greatest of these prophets, received the written and oral Torah.

Scripture

The Tenakh (known more widely as the Hebrew Bible) is a collection of 24 books, written in Hebrew, arranged in three main sections: the Torah ('teachings') which makes up the first five books, contains the instructions which G_d gave to Moses; Nevi'im (eight books) and Ketuvim (eleven books) contain histories, poems, prophecies, hymns and sayings. The Talmud, another important set of writings, contains the thoughts of some 200 rabbis. In synagogues, the Torah is kept in the form of scrolls, mounted on two wooden rollers decorated with silver heads and bells, inside a symbolic cabinet called the ark. In a service, everyone stands as the scroll is taken out, as a mark of respect for the Torah's significance in Jewish life, throughout history and today.

Worship, prayer & meditation

All devout Jews are obliged to pray daily. This is the key spiritual duty or commandment (mitzvah) which Jews are expected to honour as part of the covenant G_d made with their ancestors. Those belonging to different Jewish groups have different styles of prayer and worship, individually and collectively. The Jewish prayer book is known as the siddur; it contains a variety of written prayers, including ones for blessings, praise of G_d, the well-being of the Jewish people and of the world, and for the granting of holiness. This book may be used when praying in the synagogue or at home. Services in the synagogue tend to be fairly informal, with worshippers coming and going. Judaism has a strong tradition of meditation, contemplation and mysticism, which also can be found in a variety of forms.

Spirituality

Although it can appear to the outside observer that Judaism is a very scholarly religion, deeply concerned with commentary and interpretation of ancient law, a lot of its attention focused on ancient times, it really attends to how one should live, and what one has to do in everyday life to bear out one's beliefs. Jews cannot simply compartmentalise things into religious and non-religious topics. Most of all, Judaism focuses on how G_d's plan for all creation is expressed in relationships, across history and in the present moment: between G_d and all humankind, between G_d and the Jewish people, between the Jewish people and the land of Israel and between all human beings, down through the generations and all over the world today.

Lifestyle

Probably the best known aspect of Jewish life is the keeping of the Sabbath (Shabbat in Hebrew) from sunset on Friday to sunset on Saturday. It is the Jewish holy day, a day for rest and religious reflection. The beginning and end of the Sabbath are marked with observances that bring together the Jewish family and community. Jews follow specific dietary regulations, affecting what they are allowed to eat and drink. Jews will not eat any food from an animal that does not chew the cud, have split hooves and has not been ritually slaughtered and prepared. Fish must have fins and scales (so, for example, they will not eat shellfish). Many Jews will not mix dairy and meat products in the same meal. Food which is acceptable to Jews is called kosher (meaning 'fit').

Community

For most of its history, Judaism has accommodated a diversity of movements. Today, religious Jews fall into two broad groups: Orthodox and non-Orthodox. Differences between them can be seen in their everyday lives as well as in their forms of worship, though even these two groups show considerable variation within themselves. Orthodox Jews are traditional followers of rabbinic Judaism, although they diversify in belief and practice. Amongst non-Orthodox Jews, the moderate Conservative movement believes that laws and traditions can be adapted to suit the times but to a lesser extent than the Liberal, Progressive and Reform movements, which allow individuals varying degrees of greater freedom in relation to the traditions which they follow.

Festivals

The Jewish year has many festivals and holy days, some solemn, others celebratory, most recalling events in Jewish history. Among the more sombre observances are New Year (Rosh Hashana) and the Day of Atonement (Yom Kippur), which requires 25 hours of fasting in the synagogue, during which Jews seek divine forgiveness. During the Festival of Tabernacles (Sukkot), Jewish people erect tents or booths, open to the sky, symbols which remind them of G_d's bounty. Passover (Pesach) celebrates the exodus from slavery in Egypt, led by Moses. The Festival of Lights (Hanukkah) is an eight-day celebration in December, which is often an occasion when Jews may be joined by friends from outside their community.

Jews worldwide

The movement of Jews to various countries throughout history became known as the Dispersion. There are around 14 million Jews in the world, making it the world's 6th largest religion, with 0.22% of the global population. The largest Jewish population, of more than five-and-a-half million, is in the USA. Next biggest is Israel, with around four-and-a-half million (41% of the world's Jewish population). The most significant events in the recent history of the Jewish people have been the Holocaust and the founding of the state of Israel, both occurring around the middle years of the 20th century. These have played a huge part in determining modern Jewish identity. Today, those Jews living outside Israel are said to be living in the Jewish Diaspora.

Jews in Britain

The 2001 census records 259,927 Jews in England and Wales, half of 1% of the population. Jewish settlers are known to have arrived in Britain after the Norman conquest (1066). The Jews were expelled by Edward I in 1290 and readmitted by Cromwell in 1656. In that same year, the first synagogue was opened in Creechurch Lane, London. Most Jews in Britain are descendants of immigrants from Central and Eastern Europe, some fleeing anti-semitic persecution in the Russian Empire between 1881 and 1914, others escaping the Nazis in the 1930s. Since the mid-1950s a small number have arrived from Arab and East European countries. British Jews are mostly concentrated in Greater London, Manchester, Leeds and Glasgow. Around 60% belong to Orthodox synagogues, 27% to Reform synagogues.

Death & Bereavement

What Happens After Death?

According to Jewish tradition, the soul is a portion of G-d infused in a physical body. The G-dly soul animates and enlivens the body. It allows it to see, hear and interact with the world around it. During a person's lifetime on earth, they are given the merit and free choice to partner with their G-dly soul. They can affect it and the world, by either allowing the soul to shine forth through proper thoughts, words and deeds, or by burying it beneath layers and coverings, suppressing and tarnishing its G-dly radiance. After passing from this world, the soul is brought before the Heavenly Court to account for its actions and behaviour during its mortal lifetime.

Jews believe that there are two worlds or states: *Olam Hazeh* (this World) and *Olam Habah* (the World to Come). In Olam Hazeh, G-dliness is hidden (enabling a person to have free choice). In Olam Habah, G-dliness is completely revealed. In between those two worlds is *Gan Eden* (heaven or paradise). There the soul reposes until it is ushered into the World to Come and re-experiences as its reward the G-dliness that it brought into the world.

If the soul returns 'tarnished', it must go through a state of *Gehinom* (purgatory), in which it is made to understand the spiritual failings and vacuum caused by its lapses and transgressions, before it can enter Gan Eden. As the G-dly soul is pure and good at its essence, the experience of Gehinom never exceeds more than twelve months.

Jewish law teaches that every moment of life is extremely precious, and brings untold benefits to the soul. Therefore, the Torah obligates each person to do all that is possible to keep body and soul united, prolonging life so that the soul can complete its mission, until G-d decides it is time to collect the soul.

As Death Approaches

The returning of one's soul to G-d at the end of its journey in this world is probably the most profound moment in a person's life. It is for this purpose that sages have prepared a special set of prayers called *Viduy* (confession), which are to be recited before one departs from this world. These prayers evoke G-d's mercy and bring great atonement upon the person. Viduy reminds Jews that what really matters is their relationship with G-d and with fellow man and not material possessions or accomplishments. It is a powerful message for everyone. Its translation is as follows:

I acknowledge before You, L_rd my G-d and the G-d of my fathers, that my recovery and my death are in Your hands. May it be Your will that You heal me with total recovery but if I die, may my death be an atonement for all the errors, iniquities and wilful sins that I have erred, sinned and transgressed before You and may You grant my share in the Garden of Eden **and grant me the merit to abide in the** World to Come **which is vouchsafed for the righteous.**

Our G-d and G-d of our fathers, may our prayers come before You and do not turn away from our supplication, for we are not so impudent and obdurate as to declare before You, L_rd our G-d and G-d of our fathers, that we are righteous and have not sinned. Indeed, we and our fathers have sinned.

We have transgressed, we have acted perfidiously, we have robbed, we have slandered. We have acted perversely and wickedly, we have willfully sinned, we have done violence, we have imputed falsely. We have given evil counsel, we have lied, we have scoffed, we have rebelled, we have provoked, we have been disobedient, we have committed iniquity, we have wantonly transgressed, we have oppressed, we have been obstinate. We have committed evil, we have acted perniciously, we have acted abominably, we have gone astray, we have led others astray. We have strayed from Your good precepts and ordinances and it has

not profited us. Indeed, You are just in all that has come upon us, for You have acted truthfully and it is we who have acted wickedly.

It is best for Viduy to be recited with a clear mind. Therefore, one should say it before he becomes too weak. If one cannot speak, one may say the Viduy in their heart.

Once death seems imminent, one should not leave the person alone and those remaining should recite Psalms. One should try to ensure that the person's spouse and children are present at the moment of passing. However, only those who can contain their grief should be in the room. Those in the room should be careful not to wail or cry loudly. This causes the person who is leaving the world great pain and discomfort and prolongs their ordeal.

Once the person has entered the actual throes of death, it is forbidden to move or touch them, as this may hasten their death; in the eyes of Jewish law, it is considered as shedding blood. The exceptions are providing life-saving intervention or water for the person to drink.

At the very last moments, all present, including the person themselves (if possible), recite the following passages aloud, and with intense concentration:

"Hear, O Israel, the L-rd is our G-d, the L-rd is One"

The Moment of Death

In Judaism respect to the deceased is essential. Therefore once death occurs, a Rabbi should be contacted as soon as possible. If this is not possible for example if it is on a Saturday (the Jewish Shabbat) or a major Jewish festival, the eyes of the deceased should be closed, the body laid flat with hands open, arms laid down in line with the body and the legs should be laid out straight. Any electrical equipment attached to the body may be removed but all plasters etc. should be left. The greatest respect that can be shown towards the deceased is to do nothing further, unless cleansing of the orifices is necessary to preserve dignity. The body should then be completely covered (including the head) with a sheet, and where possible, should not be left unattended.

A beautiful and moving custom calls upon relatives and friends to ask forgiveness of the deceased, at this time, for any harm or discomfort they might have caused them during their lifetime.

Personal behaviour in the room of the deceased should be consonant with the highest degree of respect for the person. There should be no eating, drinking or smoking in their presence. Outside the room, however, these are permitted. No derogatory remarks about the deceased should be voiced. Discussion in the room should concentrate solely on the deceased and their personal qualities, or on the funeral arrangements. The Rabbi will notify the *Chevra Kadisha* (Jewish Burial Society) who will take care of the deceased. There should be no singing or playing of music and the body should remain completely covered (out of respect for the deceased), until the Burial Society arrives.

Preparing the Body

On Saturday, the body is not moved. It is covered with a sheet until the conclusion of the Shabbat. At all other times the Jewish Burial Society will arrange as soon as possible for the body to be prepared for burial. This is done with the *Tahara* (purification) process. A proper Tahara includes cleansing, ritually washing and dressing the deceased's body in simple burial shrouds. Those who perform this *Chesed Shel Emet* (true act of kindness) recite special prayers, beseeching G-d to lift the soul into the heavens and eternal rest. Males are wrapped in their Tallit (prayer shawl). These procedures will all be carried out by the Jewish Burial Society.

Once the members of the Jewish Burial Society have completed preparing the deceased for burial, the funeral can proceed.

Autopsies are strongly forbidden. In the case of a suspected crime, or other unusual situations, one must consult a Rabbi, who specialises in this area of Jewish law, for guidance. Organ donation, in general, is a very complicated matter in Jewish law. Again one must consult a Rabbi who specialises in this area of Jewish law for guidance before taking any action or making any decisions in this matter

Method of Disposal

It is forbidden to leave the deceased unburied overnight, as it states in the Torah, 'You shall bury him on that same day' (Deuteronomy 21:23). One may delay the burial for the deceased's honour, to perform the Tahara-purification, to obtain shrouds or a burial plot, or to gather close family, but not unnecessarily or for the convenience of others. Therefore Jewish burials take place as soon as possible after death. Ideally they will be on the same day and any unnecessary delays must be avoided.

According to Jewish law, cremation is not permitted in any circumstance. It is viewed as an offensive act that goes violently against the spirit and letter of Jewish law. Instead the deceased must be interred, in the earth. A simple wood coffin is used and there are no flowers or elaborate accompaniments for the funeral. Embalming and pre-funeral cosmetic surgery are all explicitly forbidden according to Jewish law. These are very serious matters and should not be treated lightly.

Funeral Customs

The family and the community gather at the cemetery. There should be at least ten Jewish males over the age of thirteen (a *Minyan*) at the service and burial. The casket is present during the service but remains closed. The Jewish custom is not to serve fancy foods nor have flowers or music at the funeral. Those items are associated with festivity and joy and this is a solemn occasion.

The Rabbi or designated Jewish person performs *Kriah* (ritual rending of the outer garments) with the mourners and begins the service by reciting Psalms. Some follow this with remarks from family members or close friends. Afterwards, some close the gathering with the traditional memorial prayer *Kel Molay Rachamim* (**O G-d, full of compassion**).

At the conclusion of the service, the mourners then proceed to the interment (burial of the body in the earth). The order of prayers at a funeral may vary according to local custom. One should follow the custom of their community, or ask a competent Rabbi for guidance.

After the interment, the grave is filled and then the closest male relative says Kaddish prayer. The Kaddish is a glorification of G-d rather than a prayer about death. The reason that this prayer is recited for someone who has passed away is to help elevate the soul in the next world.

The rites associated with death in Judaism concentrate on support for the close relatives and helping the soul of the departed be elevated in the next world.

Mourning Practices

For seven days after the funeral the family goes into mourning with the exception of Shabbat (Saturday) when there is no public mourning. This is known as sitting *Shiva*. During this period the mourners refrain from sitting on regular chairs, conducting business matters, wearing leather shoes, greeting another person, bathing for pleasure, wearing freshly laundered clothes, grooming, haircutting, shaving, and marital relations.

Friends of the mourners visit to bring food, care for the family's needs and give emotional support. A service may be held in the house daily if not three times a day. Throughout this week the bereaved family faces their loss and tries to come to terms with it. The following is a list of for whom a person is obligated to mourn: Father, mother, brother, sister, husband, wife, son, daughter.

Although the mourners return to normal life after this week, there is a thirty day period after death know as *Sheloshim*, during which they must continue to refrain from bathing for pleasure and wearing freshly-laundered clothes. One should keep in mind that this does not mean a person should not have a normal standard of hygienic care or personal dignity. The mourners should also refrain from any form of entertainment.

For eleven months following *Shanah* (the funeral) a mourner says Kaddish every day in the three daily prayer services. On every *Yarhzeit* (anniversary of the death). Kaddish is also said in the Synagogue at the daily prayer services and at home a 24-hour candle is lit, charity is given and one studies some Jewish text in memory of the departed.

The grave should be visited at least once a year. Many people have a custom of going just before the Jewish New Year (September/ October). The gravestone is usually erected during the first year after death and is marked by a short service of consecration at the cemetery.

The reduction in the intensity of mourning throughout the three periods (i.e. Shiva, Sheloshim and Shanah) is an aid to readjustment to normal life in face of the void left behind by the departed. Extending mourning beyond the above set periods is not positive and should be actively discouraged. The annual observances help to comfort the bereaved and ensure the cherished memories spur those left behind to move forward and improve in their daily conduct.

This is an account of the Jewish traditions in death and mourning distilled from over 3000 years of knowledge and understanding of human nature. However, one should be aware that a Jew as an individual may follow all, some or none of the above. Every mourner should none the less be treated with care, compassion and sensitivity as they go through these difficult times.

We are grateful to Rabbi Shmuli Pink who kindly provided the information in this section

Sikhism

Definitions

A Sikh is a person who belongs to the religion of Sikhism. 'Sikh' is usually translated as 'disciple' or 'student' and has been defined as someone who faithfully believes in one immortal Being (God), the ten historical Gurus (from Guru Nanak to Guru Gobind Singh), the Guru Granth Sahib (the collected Sikh scripture), the utterances and teachings of the ten Gurus; the baptism bequeathed by the tenth Guru, and who does not owe allegiance to any other religion. One may also use 'Sikh' to define one's cultural or national identity and heritage. The Khanda is a well-known Sikh symbol. The double-edged sword at the centre represents the power of the Creator;,the circle denotes the Creator's eternal perfection, the two outer swords stand for spiritual and political balance.

Origins

The founding father of Sikhism, Guru Nanak (1469-1539 CE) was born in the Punjab ('Land of Five Rivers') a territory now shared between northern India and Pakistan. Highly revered in his own lifetime, Guru Nanak established a spiritual community transcending distinctions of race, class, gender, ethnicity, social background and economic status. His teachings recognises all people as equals, with the right to follow their own path to God. For nigh on two centuries, nine further Gurus carried this revolutionary spiritual and social message to the masses. The tenth, Guru Gobind Singh (1666-1708) founded the Khalsa ('Pure Ones') and installed the *Guru Granth Sahib* as the eternal source of guidance. His decisive actions instituted the Sikh community in the form still recognisable today.

Beliefs

Sikhs believe in the cycle of birth, death and rebirth, dictated by the law of karma – that people are rewarded for their deeds, good and bad. Being born human gives one the opportunity to escape this otherwise endless cycle. These are beliefs that Sikhs hold in common with Hindus, Buddhists and Jains. Sikhs differ from those followers of other religions by believing in the power of repentance, prayer and love to earn God's grace and neutralise the effect of karma. Sikhs believe in one God, before whom everyone is equal and to whom everyone has direct and personal access. Sikhs recognise that truth is also to be found in other religions and believe that anyone who leads the right kind of life has the opportunity of attaining salvation.

Scripture

The Guru Granth Sahib is not simply the holy book of the Sikhs: it is their eternal guru and guide, the paramount spiritual authority in their religion, their first and central point of reference. The Adi Granth was first compiled by the fifth Guru, Arjan Dev, in 1604 in the city of Amritsar. The final version – the Guru Granth Sahib – was completed in 1705 by Guru Gobind Singh, who established it as the perpetual Guru of the Sikhs shortly thereafter. The Guru Granth Sahib is a poetic anthology, containing devotional and mystical poems in praise of God, written to the musical measures of the Indian classical system of ragas. It contains not only hymns of the Sikh Gurus but also compositions of several Muslim and Hindu mystics.

Worship, prayer & meditation

Practising Sikhs have a rich devotional life, both as individuals and communally in the Gurdwara (the Sikh place of worship). While Sikhs see God as being beyond human comprehension or description, still they pray to God as their Lord, teacher, father and protector, who cares for them personally. They regard prayer and meditation as ways of sharing in God's presence. Sikhs are encouraged to rise before dawn, bathe, then pray, using the words of Guru Nanak. Verses are recited from the Guru Granth Sahib and its hymns sung from early morning till late evening in the Gurdwara. Sikhs will normally gather for communal worship there every day, and especially on Sundays in this part of the world (because it fits with the typical working week in the West).

Spirituality

Sikhs do not believe there is any need to renounce everyday life in order to come closer to God. Sikhism is a practical and down-to-earth religion that encourages its followers to use their daily lives as a way of progressing on the spiritual path. Sikhs are encouraged to serve God by serving other people. In so doing, they have the opportunity to rid themselves of ego, pride and self-centredness. Sikhs have three obligations in their daily lives: to keep God in mind; to earn an honest living; to be generous to those in need. This allows personal freedom in deciding how they should act in the world. At the same time, they should try to avoid five vices: lust; covetousness; attachment to the things of this world; anger and pride.

Lifestyle

Sikh teachings prohibit the use of alcohol, non-prescribed drugs and tobacco. Many Sikhs are vegetarian. Those Sikhs who do eat meat will not eat any which has been prepared by kosher or halal methods. Personal cleanliness is very important to Sikhs. The turban, which keeps long hair clean and tidy, is a well-known sign of a Sikh. Uncut hair and beard, a steel bangle on the right wrist, a wooden comb to groom the hair, specially made cotton shorts and an ornamental dagger make up the 'five k's'. Initiation is required to join the Khalsa, membership of which demands a deeper level of prayer, meditation, charity and selflessness. Initiated males adopt the last name Singh ('Lion'); women take the name Kaur ('Princess').

Community

There are no individual positions of authority within the Sikh community, as a protection against egoism and corruption. The only role of note is that of the Granthi, who reads from the Guru Granth Sahib in the Gurdwara and officiates at ceremonies such as weddings and funerals. The gurdwara is the focus of Sikh community life. One of the most significant things that happens there is the langar or 'Guru's kitchen', where vegetarian food is served free of charge to everyone, sitting as equals – including anyone in attendance who does not happen to be Sikh. This is one practical way in which Sikhs demonstrate their belief in equality, generosity and charity without paying heed to differences of religion, caste, age, gender or social standing.

Festivals

Sikhs use their festivals as occasions on which to rededicate their faith. One such is Bandi Chhorrh Divas (which coincides with Diwali, a traditional Indian celebration also observed, in different ways, by Hindus and Jains). This marks the anniversary of the sixth guru, Guru Hargobind (1595-1644) rescuing fifty two Hindu kings from imprisonment in a celebrated act of courage. Gurpurbs are feast days honouring the birth, martyrdom or life events of the Gurus, for example, the birthday of Guru Nanak, traditionally celebrated in November as well as the installation of the Guru Granth Sahib. Vaisakhi (or Baisakhi) is the Sikh new year, on the date of a long-established harvest festival in the Punjab. It is of particular significance for commemorating the founding of the Khalsa in 1699.

Sikhs worldwide

Sikhism is the world's fifth largest religion, with more than 26 million followers worldwide. By far the majority of these live in the Punjab region. The Punjab is also the site of Harmandir Sahib(the 'House of God') – the Golden Temple at Amritsar. This is the most important site in the Sikh world, with a long and fascinating spiritual, political and military history, stretching as far back as the time of the Buddha. Gurdwaras throughout the globe fly the Nishan Sahib outside their building. This flag shows the Khanda in the middle of an orange background. It is a visual reminder of the unity of the Sikh community all over the world. There are large Sikh populations in Canada, the US, UK, Malaysia and Singapore.

Sikhs in Britain

The first recorded Sikh settler here was Duleep Singh, a young prince who came to England in exile in 1849 and settled in Thetford, Norfolk. The Prince of Wales unveiled a statue in his honour there, one hundred and fifty years later. The first Gurdwara in this country was established in 1911, at Putney. Sikh migration to Britain began in earnest in the 1930s, with men from the Punjab filling British industry's need for unskilled labour. Sikhs who had fought for the British army in the First World War came here from the Punjab after India became independent in 1948, followed later by thousands of Sikhs from East Africa. At the time of the 2001 Census, there were 336,179 Sikhs in Britain – just over half of 1% of the population.

Death & Bereavement

What Happens After Death?

Sikhs believe that upon death one merges back into the universal nature, just as a drop of rain merges back into the ocean. Individuality is lost. Sikhs do not believe in heaven or hell. Heaven can be experienced by being in tune with God while still alive. Conversely, the suffering and pain caused by the ego is seen as hell on earth. In Sikhism, spiritual pursuits as positive experiences in and of themselves that transcend death, not as sacrifices made in order to collect a reward that is waiting until after death.

The ultimate spiritual achievement in Sikhism is the complete elimination of ego. By definition, when this occurs the person intuitively become one with the Soul of the universe. When someone dies, the last vestiges of separation are removed and complete union with God results.

Sikhs are encouraged to remain mindful of and reflect upon death, as it impacts on how they live their lives. This can be demonstrated in verses from Sikh scriptures;

'The dawn of a new day is herald of a sunset. Earth is not your permanent home' (AG793)

'Death does not wait for auspicious days or ask whether it is the light or dark side of the month. Some people are harshly treated, others are well cared for. Some leave armies and mansions to the sound of drums. Nanak the heap of dust is returning to dust' (AG 1244)

As such, death is viewed as part of God's plan and so should not be feared. However Sikhs do not believe that they need to leave this world to attain salvation; this can also be achieved whilst living, through God-consciousness and good actions.

Like Hindus, Sikhs believe in reincarnation, but if a Sikh has lived a good and pious life they can break the cycle of re-birth and instead be raised to eternal bliss to be with their Creator. Sikhs believe that just as God's love is eternal, so is one's relationship with Him.

As Death Approaches

It is important for friends and family to be with their loved one when close to death. Not only does this demonstrate their love for them, but it is also part of one's religious responsibility towards them. Relatives will often recite from the Sikh sacred scriptures *Guru Granth Sahib* at this time, as this provides comfort for themselves as well as serenity for the departing soul. It is also important for the dying person to recite or hear the name of God being recited in their final stages. Family and friends can help with this.

Sometimes the *Kirtan Sohila* the 'song of peace' is recited at this time. This is a prayer, comprising of hymns from different Gurus, and is commonly said at night before going to sleep. It is also recorded in the Guru Granth Sahib.

The Moment of Death

The body of the deceased should not be moved to the floor as is done in some faith traditions, nor should any lamp be lit beside it. (This is a specification of the 'Sikh *Reht Maryada*' – The Code of Sikh Conduct.

Those present should try to remain composed. Wailing and crying aloud is strongly discouraged. Instead those present are encouraged to recite the *Gurbani* (Guru Granth Sahib) or the mantra words *Waheguru, Waheguru* (a term commonly used in Sikhism to refer to God, translated literally as 'Wondrous God'*)*, to help maintain their composure and remind themselves that this is God's will.

Preparing the Body

Often close members of the family of the same sex will wash the body of the deceased, dress him/her in clean clothes and place in the coffin. If the deceased underwent the ritual of *Amrit* (baptism to the Sikh faith), then the five symbols of Sikhism; the *Karra* (iron bracelet), the *Kaschera* (a special type of undergarment), *Kesh* (uncut hair), *Kirpan* (sword) and *Kanga* (small wooden comb) should not be taken off during process. The body is then lifted and put in the casket, and *Ardas* (a Sikh supplication/prayer said before undertaking a significant task) is recited before taking the body to the deceased's home.

The cover of the casket or coffin is placed in such a way as to enable the face still to be viewed for a short while and final farewells to be said. Sometimes the body is also taken to the Gurdwara, where the *Granthi* (a Sikh Priest / scholar) will say prayers and sprinkle with *amrit* (holy water composed of water and sugar and used in baptism of Sikhs, literally translated as 'nectar'). The coffin is then put in a hearse, and whilst travelling to the cremation ground, hymns that encourage feelings of detachment are said.

Method of Disposal

It is believed that Guru Nanak did not actually specify how the body should be dealt with and that he was indifferent to burial or cremation, what mattered more was the state of the soul. Sikhs preferred method is cremation and this is what is specified in the Sikh Reht Maryada (Sikh code of Conduct).

Funeral Customs

In India the cremation will normally be performed on an open wood log pyre. In Western Countries this will be performed at the crematorium. The coffin is placed in the cremator, whilst Ardas (supplication prayer) about consigning the body to the fire is offered. The cremator will have been turned on usually by the eldest Son, or by close relative or friend of the deceased, whilst the remaining congregation recite prayers of detachment or sing hymns, if possible observing the process from a distance.

When the flames are at their peak, the 'song of peace' prayer - the Kirtan Sohila (as mentioned previously) is recited, and the same Ardas is offered again. The congregation then leave.

The ashes are collected later, with the bone remains, and scattered in running water (a river or sea), whilst prayers are recited.

Mourning Practices

Rather than be viewed as an occasion of great sadness and distress, Sikhs are encouraged to remember that death should be looked upon as the time that the soul re-unites with his Creator. Men will usually wear black headscarves to the funeral and women wear pale coloured or white headscarves.

After the cremation, mourners will often assemble at the Gurdwara or a private venue to listen to the recitation of the Sikh holy poems. A reading of the Guru Granth Sahib is commenced, and after the first six stanzas of the *Anand Sahib* have been read, Ardas is offered, and the distribution of *Karhah Prashad* (sweet bread/pudding symbolising God's blessings) commences.

The period of mourning continues for ten days, in which time the entire reading of the Guru Granth Sahib should ideally be completed (This is usually done by close relatives of the deceased). It is believed that this is for the benefit and comfort of the bereaved family more than for the soul of the dead person who will already be united with God. Friends and family will often help out with food and other arrangements during this period.

Several rituals commonly practised, are in fact contrary to the approved code of Sikh conduct, such as *Adh Marg,* breaking the pot of water used for bathing the body, organised lamentation by women, ritual donating of lumps of rice, picking the burnt bones for immersing in the Ganga or elsewhere. These should thus be avoided.

Post-mortems and Organ Transplants

Although post-mortems and 'unnecessary' handling of the body is disliked, the principle of using organs to benefit others is not forbidden in Sikhism. As with all patients this will be subject to the decision of the next of kin.

We are grateful to Jasvir Kaur Chohan & Resham Singh Sandhu for their input towards this section

Understanding and Coping with Bereavement

Although it's difficult today to see beyond the sorrow,
May looking back in memory help comfort you tomorrow.
Author Unknown

Grieving is the natural response to a bereavement, however the experience of grief is unique to every individual. The whirlpool of emotions experienced and the process of mourning is influenced by several factors. There are many theories and models of grief that explain the stages or phases through which people pass following the death of a loved one. There is also much debate on the process involved in the healthy adaptation to the loss, as to whether the person, moves on, overcomes, forgets or gets over grief. An individual who experiences bereavement may pass through some stages or phases of grief which is determined by a variety of personal, social, cultural and contextual factors that can lead to adjustment and personal growth. In the event of complicated grief the person could be stuck in any of the phases and have difficulty with adjusting to the loss.

According to Richard Wilson (1993) Bereavement is what happens to you (the loss), Grief is what you feel (emotionally and physically) and Mourning is what you do (during this period of experiencing grief and adapting to the loss). The diagram below (ibid, 1993) depicts life as a river that flows, a sudden fall that is out of control changing the course, a whirlpool of mixed emotion, the possibility of being stuck on the river bank or flowing on to acceptance and reorganisation.

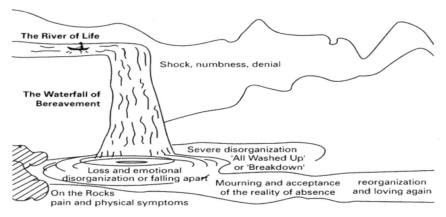

The River of Life

Shock, numbness, denial

The Waterfall of Bereavement

Severe disorganization
'All Washed Up'
or 'Breakdown'

Loss and emotional
disorganization or falling apart

Mourning and acceptance
of the reality of absence

reorganization
and loving again

On the Rocks
pain and physical symptoms

Bereavement is what happens to you; grief is what you feel; mourning is what you do.

Authors such as Lindemann (1944), Kubler-Ross (1969), Parkes (1975) and Bowlby (1981) recognise and discuss the stages of grief that begin with shock, denial or numbness ending in resolution, acceptance, recovery or adjustment (see Appendix A). The bereaved need not necessarily progress through these stages step by step, but emphasis is on the person finally integrating the loss into his or her life, marking the healthy adaptation to the life event.

> *When you are sorrowful look again in your heart,*
> *and you shall see that in truth you are weeping*
> *for that which has been your delight.*
> *Kahlil Gibran*

People can experience a range of emotions, thoughts/cognitions and behavioural changes during the process of mourning.

- Emotions – sadness, anger, guilt, anxiety, loneliness, fatigue, numbness, helplessness, shock, yearning, emancipation or relief (if following prolonged illness).

- Thoughts/cognitions – disbelief, confusion, preoccupation, sense of presence, and hallucinations.

- Behavioural changes – sleep, appetite, forgetful, social withdrawal, dreams of the deceased, avoiding memories of the deceased, searching and calling out for the deceased, restless hyperactivity, crying, visiting places, holding onto or carrying objects that reminds the survivor of the deceased, and treasuring objects of deceased.

The emotional impact of the loss on the bereaved person is also based on the context of the death

- Single loss of life or multiple as in the case of natural (earthquakes, hurricanes, tsunami, drought, heat wave, epidemic), accidental (traffic, fire) and planned (suicides, war, terror attacks), e.g. when an individual loses several members of the family.

- Instantaneous, following a prolonged illness or an act of suicide

- Early in life or at end of life

- Loss can also occur without a body being present as in the case of plane crashes/natural disasters and abductions/missing persons

- The loss of life can lead to further loss extending to health, relationships, vocation, finances and/or possessions

For some individuals and families it could be uncomplicated grief, and for others it could be traumatic/complicated grief. The ways of mourning and coping with life there on is varied based on the circumstances of the death;

as well as the individual factors of the bereaved person (resilience, strengths in problem solving and mentally adjusting to change); social (supports familial and social); and cultural context (Dillenburger & Keenan, 2005). The intensity of grief experienced is also heavily influenced by the level of attachment that one has had to the individual, which makes the 'experience of grief' unique even within one family facing the same death.

A demise that occurs in circumstances where there is reduced attachment when relationships go awry: e.g. a parent that considers the child dead, a child that rejects the parents due to disappointment of expectations of the parent, or a parent that does not maintain contact with a child following a relationship breakdown with the spouse. When a death occurs in circumstances with reduced/severed attachment, grieving may be complicated due to anger and/or guilt based on the circumstances of the death, requiring therapeutic support. In other cases there could be the absence of grief due to lack of attachment and the person may not necessarily experience grief, and this failure to experience distress is not indicative of pathology (Wortman & Silver, 1989).

> *We must embrace pain and burn it as fuel for our journey.*
> *Kenji Miyazawa*

Most individuals and families cope with loss with the support of their family, social networks and religious/cultural rituals. However for some individuals, if grief continues for an extended period of time that the individual or family feels extra support is required, counselling would be of benefit. In such cases the counsellor would work closely with the individual and family. If grief continues to impact on the life of the individual beyond this stage, then psychological therapy is sought due to the risk of grief developing into clinical depression. Therapeutic support is most often sought in cases of complicated grief and involves the bereaved person being supported to use therapeutic strategies to help adapt to the loss.

Several authors have commented on how to support the individual towards integrating the loss. According to Attig (1996) death can shatter the core of life's purpose and it's important to discover and invent new meaning in the face of loss. Neimeyer (1999) agrees with this position on the need to make meaning after the loss. This is seen in the philanthropic actions of Graham and Mary Storrie who invested their energy on the Rosie May Orphanage for Children in Sri Lanka following the tragic death of their 10 year old daughter Rosie May (2003) in Leicester, UK.

Davis, Nolen-Hoeksema & Larson (1998) describe the need to make sense of the event and find benefit in the experience, as playing a role in the adjustment process. To adjust means to change, and according to Parkes (1972) every change involves a loss and a gain. This is indicative of the bereaved individual taking on more responsibility in the absence of the loved one (e.g. learning to drive and be independent, attending to banking and taking control of finances, etc) thereby feeling empowered. Following the Asian Tsunami (2004), it was remarkable to see the way in which people made sense of the death and destruction and found new meaning in their experience. This is seen in the actions of a group of young survivors who teamed up (Rebuilding Lives Project, 2005) to provide mental health support to the community through the Foundation of Goodness, a leading charity in Sri Lanka.

Stroebe & Schut (1999) speaks on how it is important that the person at times confronts and at other times avoids the tasks of grieving, and the need to take respite of these stressors as an integral part of adaptive coping. This is evident in the words of a man who lost his mother and his wife in the Asian Tsunami, 'I throw myself into community work or I will be overwhelmed by sorrow. I take time to grieve at night and share my feelings with my friends ...... and now I have my daughter's future to look after'.

Counselling and Psychological therapy deals with those who are left behind. Therefore the focus is on supporting the bereaved person to cope with and adjust to a life with meaning in the absence of their loved one. Worden (1991) provides four dynamic and functional tasks (not stages or phases) that help with the processing grief.

1. Accept the reality of the loss
2. Process the pain of grief
3. Adjust to life without the deceased
4. Find an enduring connection with the deceased whilst embarking on a new life

To live in hearts we leave behind is not to die
Campbell (1777-1844)

The person will respond to the loss based on several factors. Therefore it is important for the helping professional to get a good understanding of (Worden, 2008):

- The person who died and the quality of the relationship to the bereaved

- The strength and quality of the attachment to the deceased

- The circumstances of the death

- Historical aspects of bereaved individual (mental health difficulties, family issues, conflicts)

- Personality aspects related to gender; age; coping style (problem solving; active coping using humour and reframing events, venting the positives and negatives of the deceased; emotional expression (avoidant emotional coping involving blaming, denial, withdrawal, distraction); attachment styles (secure/ insecure, anxious, preoccupied, ambivalent, avoidant, dismissive, fearful)l; cognitive style (positive and negative); ego strength (self efficacy and esteem); assumptions and beliefs (self, others, world)

- Social factors such as support available, social role, religious and ethnic expectations.

Worden (2008) recommends that the bereaved person be supported through the four tasks, by increasing the reality of loss; helping to deal with emotional and behavioural pain; helping overcome impediments to readjustment; helping to find a way to maintain the bond while reinvesting in life.

- Sighting the body – whether it is at the hospital or at the funeral, brings the reality of the fact that the person has died into focus.

- Funeral – making arrangements for the funeral, participating in the funeral, religious and cultural rituals provides a forum for friends and family to express their sorrow and where appropriate share cherished memories and sentiments of the deceased.

- Language – using words such as 'died' instead of 'loss' and referring to the person in the past tense 'when he *was* working at', helps with adjusting to the fact that the person has died.

- Symbols – such as photos, letters written by deceased, clothing, video and audio tapes help to concretise the focus of discussion rather than thinking of the diseased in the abstract.

- Symbolic activity – planting trees, releasing balloons, taking flowers to the grave, charity in memory of the loved one.

- Writing –letter expressing thoughts/feelings to the deceased helps to take care of unfinished business; writing poetry; keeping a journal of grief experience.

- Drawing – pictures that reflect feelings and any conflict within.

- Role play – aspects that the bereaved person can find fearful and awkward e.g. needing to explain something or express emotion.

- Cognitive restructuring through cognitive strategies (Hettiarachchi, 2007) –self talk, confronting and challenging thinking about the deceased, the loss and life without the deceased; enjoying the fond memories

- Emotional processing - acknowledge that it is alright to feel bad from time to time and talk about these feelings.

You're only here for a short visit
So be sure to stop and smell the flowers
Walter Hagen (1892-1969)

- Adjusting to a world without the deceased - through everyday functioning; being aware of how the death affects one's sense of self; and how the death affects beliefs, values, and assumptions. These activities help redefine the loss, find meaning, and learn new skills to continue life and accept the past.

- Finding space within oneself to emotionally relocate the deceased – it is not about forgetting the dead person, but supporting the bereaved to find a special psychological space within that allows the memory to be cherished that creates space for others and to gradually feel comfortable with life.

The death of a loved one can cause a person to experience a form of death before the person begins to grow through this experience and readjust to the task of living. Life would never be the same again as surely as, 'you could not step twice into the same river; for other waters are ever flowing on to you' (Heraclitus, 535 BCE - 475 BCE). What is vital to remember is that whilst grief is unique to each individual based on personal, social, and contextual factors, it has some common elements. The bereaved needs to be supported to adjust to the major life event either formally or informally. This work requires sensitivity and flexibility of understanding as there is no clear time frame or recipe for people to integrate the loss and adjust to change.

I expect to pass through life but once. If therefore, there be any kindness I can show, or any good thing I can do to any fellow being, let me do it now, and not defer or neglect it, as I shall not pass this way again.

William Penn (1644-1718)

Stages/phases of bereavement						Targets in the healing process
Lindeman (1944)	Kubler-Ross (1969)	Parkes (1975)	Bowlby (1981)	Sanders (1989)	Wilson (1993)	Worden (1991)
Shock	Denial	Numbness	Numbing	Shock	Shock, numb, denial	Acceptance of loss
Acute mourning	Anger	Searching/ pining	Yearning	Awareness of loss	Disorganisation	Working though the pain of grief
Resolution	Bargaining	Depression	Disorganisation and despair	Conservation withdrawal	Mourning and acceptance	Adjusting to life without the deceased
	Depression	Recovery	Organisation Adjustment	Healing	Reorganisation – loving again	Emotionally relocate the deceased and move on with life - Reinvestment in new life
	Acceptance			Renewal		

Malkanthi Hettiarachchi (MAPS)
BA (Hons) Psychology, MSc (Mental Health), MSc (Clinical Psychology)

References on page 179

Acknowledgements

The creation of this book was ambitious. The mere fact of its existence is testimony to the great and unerring support that I have received from my friends and colleagues from the many different faith and non-faith communities. I attempt to recognise and thank all those that helped me in this work. Please forgive me if you feel you have been omitted, and any such omission was unintentional.

We have demonstrated once again that the United Kingdom is at the cutting edge of promoting positive relationships between its communities and that we have moved from dialogue to action. It is my hope that this book will offer a blueprint to the rest of the Europe as to how communities can work together on matters of common concern.

I have been motivated by my beliefs as a Muslim and also by those things that are not exclusive to Islam. I feel that we have to continue to learn how we can create a society built on love and peace whilst we all remain faithful to each of our traditions. Interest in this work has been shown by many organisations abroad. Therefore it is a matter of great joy that we have exported good British practice to other countries. This fills us with immense pride.

This publication is clear evidence of the mutual cooperation and trust that now exists between our many faith groups. This is the result of the many years of dialogue that we have engaged in. I am deeply grateful to the following individuals which have been key contributors. They all gave me their valuable time.

Those that took part in personal interviews and verified the material for publication are:

Allan Hayes; Eleanor Davidson; Father John Lally; Hemang Bhatt; Jasvir Kaur Chohan; Maganbhai Mashru; Minou Cortazzi; Narandasbhai Adati;,

Ramanbhai Barbar; Rameshbhai Majithia; Rashmibhai Joshi; Resham Singh Sandhu; Rev. David Clark; Smita Shah; Susthama Kim

Those that contributed with written statements:

Dr.Shanthikumar Hettiarachchi; Rabbi Shmuli Pink; Ven. Teldeniyaye Amitha;

I would like to acknowledge our key financial supporters who have made a crucial contribution and without their support this would have been impossible.

Leicester City Council

MBCOL has a long standing relationship with Leicester City Council as it has helped in the creation of the organisation. This partnership between a public sector and community sector organisation has made a major contribution towards improving community cohesion in Leicester. Previous Council administrations also deserve thanks for supporting the work of MBCOL throughout their term of office.

The City Council has already supported MBCOL to create 'Guidelines on Death and Burial of a Muslim', our first booklet explaining the customs, traditions and implications when a Muslim passes away. This pioneering booklet gave us the idea and determination to produce a follow up booklet to include other faith communities. Leicester City Council have provided us with funding for this particular task and for that, all faith communities, people of no faith, employers and public sector organisations should be grateful as the booklet will give them an insight into better service provision and good employment practice.

I would like to personally express my sincere gratitude to:

The Leader of Leicester City Council, Councillor Veejay Patel; Councillor Ross Willmott; Councillor Roger Blackmore; Councillor Abdul Osman;

Councillor Mohammed Dawood; Councillor Hussein Suleman; Councillor Hanif Aqbany; Councillor Iqbal Desai; Councillor Parmjit Singh Gill; Councillor Shofiqul Chowdhury; Councillor Piara Singh Clair

The officers of the Leicester City/council that have played a crucial role are many, a few however, deserve a mention namely:

Chief Executive Sheila Lock; Lee Harrison; Richard Welburn; Lisa Handy; Trish Roberts-Thomson; Cathy Carter; Sheena Raval

Leicestershire Constabulary

Through its former *Chief Constable, Matt Baggott*, and his successors, the force is committed to the faith communities of Leicester. It is in this supportive environment that our engagement with the Police has fashioned positive outcomes and added to a greater understanding both within and between our diverse communities. I would like to acknowledge the following:

Matt Baggott; Chief Constable Simon Cole; Chief Supt Chris Garnham; Commander of Central Region, Paul Smith; Rik Basra; Rob Nixon; Steve Bolton of the Force Community Safety Bureau; Inspector Shane O'Neill; PC Catharine Thompson

Bereavement is an extremely stressful period for all concerned. It is also however, a time when statutory obligations need to be addressed. It is important that Police officers involved during these trying times deal with issues in an appropriate way. The training for officers that has been put in place to meet the sensitivities of the Muslim community has to be commended. You will not be surprised therefore to find an article contributed by the Police in this ground breaking publication.

It is also appropriate that I recognise and thank them not only for their financial assistance but also the enthusiasm that I have had in this project from all of their lead officers and also the positive support that I have had from *Chris Eyre, the Deputy Chief Constable.*

The manner in which the Police have engaged with the MBCOL serves as a positive model that is worthy of emulation elsewhere in our country. Recent national and international events and the potential dynamics effecting community cohesion make such an approach vital.

Voluntary Action Leicester (VAL)

I recognise the valuable contribution and support of VAL. Apart from the direct financial support that we have received for this publication, the relationship between MBCOL and VAL goes back a long way. VAL has assisted MBCOL in its formation over a decade ago and assisted us to create our first Constitution. MBCOL also recognises VAL's contribution and advice on regulatory compliance, guidance on best practice, governance, accountability and funding.

Through its funding of this project, VAL has played a pivotal role in drawing attention to the vital role that matters of faith play in our society. Our experience has shown that faith and secular organisations frequently work together to tackle discrimination and to build stronger communities. We are aware that VAL, through its other work, has recognised the many faith communities in Leicester and helped to build strong interfaith networks in the city. My thanks to *Carol Varley, Angela Riley* and colleagues for their patience and understanding.

Leicester City Primary Care Trust

I recognise that any success in our work can only be achieved with the help of certain key partners. In this area the medical profession and the allied institutions have been vital in the work that we have done and will remain important in the years going forward. In this regard the financial support from the Leicester City Primary Care Trust has been very valuable and I would express my sincere thanks to *Mr Phillip Parkinson* and his board members in their positive response to this publication.

The George Ernest Ellis Foundation

MBCOL also recognises the financial support that we have received from the Foundation and I know that they play a vital role in assisting various groups in our county. I would thank the foundation for their encouragement and support in respect of this publication.

Special Thanks

Others who have contributed in a significant way are deserving of a special thank you. They are:

Alexis Wood (Leicester City Council); Andrew Wingate; Angela Wingate; Barrie Thurlow; Catherine Mason; Department of Health; Elizabeth Wayne; Foreign and Commonwealth Office; Gillian Hall; Home Office; Leicestershire Constabulary; Maureen Hepburn (Salvation Army); Ministry of Justice; Philip Webster; Phillip Parkinson; Professor Guy Rutty (University of Leicester); Robert Walker, (East Midlands Ambulance Service); Sir Peter Soulsby MP

I have to acknowledge the valuable contribution made by colleagues and friends who worked tirelessly to help make our wish become a reality. Without their active contributions this publication would not have been possible, they are;

Dr. Rashed Akhtar; Faizal Essat; Rabiha Hannan; Riaz Ravat; Salim Mangera

I believe that this work is an exceptional project in that the issues in this publication touch the lives of 'people on the street' in a meaningful way. I hope that we can build on this groundbreaking work so that other community projects can be delivered in future in other areas of work.

I believe that we must explore our knowledge about each other. This is embedded in my faith and through a process of engagement with others, I am able to fortify my own faith, in a way it is a voyage of self discovery and a journey that strengthens my faith. I know this from the declaration in the Qur'an:

"O mankind! We have created you from a male and a female, and made you into nations and tribes, that you may know one another." [Sura 49 - Verse 13]

This verse underlines that we as people must recognise our humanity and we should learn to "know one another". It is therefore a natural conclusion I draw that we have to understand and to engage with each other. In the development of our own community we owe a great deal to others. My faith teaches me to believe in things that I cannot see and that there should be peace within every heart. We must all remain faithful to the hope of our future and never lose sight of those things that make us all the same. We must continue to challenge ourselves and believe that many things are possible even if we are told that they are not.

I hope that you will share the importance I have placed on this work. I hope that we will continue to forge stronger relationships and maintain the momentum that we have all jointly created.

For me personally, my encounter with others has fortified my own faith and relationship with Allah. I pray that we may we all grow in the spirit of humanity and good works with our fellow man.

Suleman Nagdi MBE JP DL

References to *Understanding and Coping with Bereavement*

1. Asian Tsunami. (2004). Retrieved 1 February, 2009, from http://en.wikipedia.org/wiki/2004_Indian_Ocean_earthquake

2. Attig, T. (1996). How we grieve: Relearning the world. Oxford: Oxford University Press.

3. Bowlby, J. (1981). Attachment and Loss. London: Penguin.

4. Dillenburger, K., & Keenan, M. (2005). Bereavement: A DISC Analysis. *Behaviour and Social Issues*, *14,* 92-112.

5. Davis, C.G., Nolen-Hoeksema, S., & Larson, J. (1998). Making sense of loss and benefiting from the experience: Two construals of meaning. *Journal of Personality and Social Psychology, 75*(2), 561-574.

6. Hettiarachchi, M. (2007). Brief intervention for Post Traumatic Stress Disorder with combined use of Cognitive Behaviour Therapy and Eye Movement Desensitisation Reprocessing. *Australian e-Journal for the Advancement of Mental Health, 6*(1), www.auseinet.com/journal/vol6iss1/hettiarachchi.pdf

7. Heraclitus. (535 BC - 475 BC). http://en.wikiquote.org/wiki/Heraclitus

8. Kubler-Ross, E. (1969). On Death and Dying. London, Macmillan.

9. Lindemann, E. (1944). Symptomatology and management of acute grief. *American Journal of Psychiatry, 101*, 141-148.

10. Neimeyer, R. (1999). Narrative strategies in grief therapy. *Journal of Constructive Psychology, 12,* 65-85.

11. Parkes, C.M. (1972). Bereavement: Studies of grief in adult life. London: Tavistock.

12. Parkes, C.M. (1975). Bereavement: Studies of Grief in Adult Life. Harmondsworth: Penguin.

13. Rebuilding Lives Project. (2005). Foundation of Goodness. Retrieved 1 February, 2009, from www.unconditionalcompassion.org

14. Rosie May. (2003). Retrieved 1 February, 2009, from http://www.rosie-may.com/

15. Sanders, C.M. (1989). Grief: The mourning after. New York: John Wiley and Sons, Inc.

16. Stroebe, M., & Schut, H. (1999). The dual process model of coping with bereavement: rationale and description. *Death Studies, 23*(3), 197-224.

17. Wilson, R. (1993). The whirlpool of grief. In Spall, B., & Callis, S. (1997). Loss, Bereavement and Grief: A Guide to Effective Caring. Cheltenham: Stanley Thornes.

18. Worden, W. (1991). Grief Counselling and Grief Therapy: A Handbook for the Mental Health Practitioner. London: Tavistock/Routledge.

19. Worden, W.J. (2008). Grief Counselling and Grief Therapy: A Handbook for the Mental Health Practitioner. New York: Springer Publishing Company.

20. Wortman, C.B., & Silver, R.C. (1989). The myths of coping with loss. *Journal of Consulting and Clinical Psychology, 57*(3), 349-357.

Other Resources Consulted

1. Asian Tsunami. (2004). http://en.wikipedia.org/wiki/ 2004_Indian_Ocean_earthquake

2. Attig, T. (1996). *How we grieve: Relearning the world.* Oxford: Oxford University Press.

3. Badham, Paul & Ballard, Paul (1996). *Facing Death.* Cardiff: University of Wales press.

4. Bowlby, J. (1981). *Attachment and Loss.* London: Penguin.

5. Cobb, Mark (2001). *The Dying Soul.* Buckingham: Open University Press

6. Cropper, Tom Funeral Service Times (March 2008). *Rites of Passage, Sikh view of death.* P.36.

7. Davis, C.G., Nolen-Hoeksema, S., & Larson, J. (1998). *Making sense of loss and benefiting from the experience*: Two construal's of meaning. *Journal of Personality and Social Psychology, 75*(2), 561-574.

8. Department of Health

9. Dharam Parchar Committee (1997). *Sikh Reht Maryada.* The Code of Sikh Conduct & Conventions. Amritsar: Golden Offset Press

10. Dillenburger, K., & Keenan, M. (2005). *Bereavement*: A DISC Analysis. *Behaviour and Social Issues, 14,* 92-112.
11. Downie, R.S. & Calman, K.C. (1994). *Healthy Respect, ethics in health care.* Oxford: Oxford University Press.

12. Foreign Commonwealth Office

13. Harish Haria, Sandya (2002). *Shraddhanjali.* Herts: Oshwal Association of the UK.

14. Heraclitus. (535 BC - 475 BC). http://en.wikiquote.org/wiki/Heraclitus

15. Hettiarachchi, M. (2007). *Brief intervention for Post Traumatic Stress Disorder with combined use of Cognitive Behaviour Therapy and Eye Movement Desensitisation Reprocessing. Australian e-Journal for the Advancement of Mental Health, 6*(1), www.auseinet.com/journal/vol6iss1/ hettiarachchi.pdf

16. http://www.humanism.org.uk

17. Kariyawasam A.G.S. (1995). *Buddhist ceremonies and rituals in Sri Lanka.* Buddhist publication society, Kandy

18. Kubler-Ross, E. (1969). *On Death and Dying.* London, Macmillan.

19. *Kuddaka nikaya.* 1.7.

20. Lindemann, E. (1944). *Symptomatology and management of acute grief.* American Journal of Psychiatry, 101, 141-148.

21. Malaysian Buddhist Cooperation Society, Malaysia (1993). *A guide to a proper Buddhist funeral*

22. Ministry of Justice

23. http://www.direct.gov.uk/en/Governmentcitizensandrights/Death/index.htm

24. http://www.direct.gov.uk/en/Governmentcitizensandrights/Death/WhatToDoAfterADeath/index.htm

25. Neimeyer, R. (1999). *Narrative strategies in grief therapy*. Journal of Constructive Psychology, 12, 65-85.

26. Nesbitt, Paula D (2001). *Religion and Social Policy*. USA: Alta Mira Press

27. Neuberger, Julia (2004). *Caring for Dying People of Different Faiths*. Oxford: Radcliffe Medical Press Ltd.

28. Neuberger, Julia (2004). *Dying Well, a guide to enabling a good death*. Oxford: Radcliffe Publishing.

29. Parkes, C.M. (1972). *Bereavement: Studies of grief in adult life*. London: Tavistock.

30. Parkes, C.M. (1975). *Bereavement: Studies of Grief in Adult Life*. Harmondsworth: Penguin.

31. Piyadassi, Ven. (1994). *The Buddhist doctrine of after life*. Corporate Body of the Buddha Educational foundation, Taiwan

32. Ravat, R. (2004). *Embracing the present, planning the future, social action by the faith communities of Leicester*

33. Rebuilding Lives Project. (2005). *Foundation of Goodness*. Retrieved 1 February, 2009, from www.unconditionalcompassion.org

34. Rosie May. (2003). Retrieved 1 February, 2009, from http://www.rosie-may.com/
35.
36. Sanders, C.M. (1989). *Grief: The mourning after*. New York: John Wiley and Sons, Inc.

37. Sheikh, Aziz & Gatrad, Abdul Rashid (2001). *Caring for Muslim Patients*. Oxford: Radcliffe Medical Press Ltd.

38. Singapore Hindu Online. Hindu death rites: suggested guidelines. http://services.eng.uts.edu.au/~ravir/HINDU%20DEATH%20RITES%20GUIDELINE.pdf (accessed: 20th June 2008)

39. Sri Dhammananda, Ven . K. (2000). *The Buddhist way*. The Corporate Body of the Buddha Educational foundation: Taiwan

40. Sri. Dhammananda, Ven. K. *Life is uncertain death is certain.* Sasana Abhiwurdhi Wardana Society, USA

41. Stroebe, M., & Schut, H. (1999). *The dual process model of coping with bereavement: rationale and description.* Death Studies, 23(3), 197-224.

42. Thera, Narada (1973). *The Buddha and his teachings.* Singapore Buddhist meditation centre, Singapore

43. Thera, Narada (1982). *Buddhism in a Nutshell.* Corporate Body of the Buddha Educational foundation, Taiwan

44. Visuddhacara, Bhikku. *Loving and dying.* Malaysian Buddhist Cooperation Society: Malaysia.

45. Wilby, Sally. Funeral Service Times (March 2008). (What's so funny 'bout) *Peace, Love and Understanding.* P.30.

46. Wilson, R. (1993). *The whirlpool of grief.* In Spall, B., & Callis, S. (1997). *Loss, Bereavement and Grief: A Guide to Effective Caring.* Cheltenham: Stanley Thornes.

47. Worden, W. (1991). *Grief Counselling and Grief Therapy*: A Handbook for the Mental Health Practitioner. London: Tavistock/Routledge.

48. Worden, W.J. (2008). *Grief Counselling and Grief Therapy*: A Handbook for the Mental Health Practitioner. New York: Springer Publishing Company.

49. Wortman, C.B., & Silver, R.C. (1989). *The myths of coping with loss.* Journal of Consulting and Clinical Psychology, 57(3), 349-357.